LADY JANE GREY

Reluctant Queen

Also by Marguerite Vance

MARIE ANTOINETTE, DAUGHTER OF AN EMPRESS

THE LEES OF ARLINGTON

PATSY JEFFERSON OF MONTICELLO

MARTHA, DAUGHTER OF VIRGINIA

WHILE SHEPHERDS WATCHED

CAPITALS OF THE WORLD

PAULA

PAULA GOES AWAY TO SCHOOL

MARTA

A STAR FOR HANSI

Lady Jane Grey

RELUCTANT QUEEN

By

MARGUERITE VANCE

Illustrated by

NEDDA WALKER

NEW YORK

E. P. DUTTON & COMPANY, INC.

Seventh Printing March 1966

Library of Congress Catalog Card Number: 52-8246

For

ANNE SHEFFIELD

CONTENTS

ACKNOWLEDGMENT

Acknowledgment is made to the following for help in preparing the manuscript:

ROYAL ELIZABETH, E. Thornton Cook, E. P. Dutton, 1929.

HENRY THE EIGHTH, Francis Hackett, Horace Liveright, Inc., 1929.

CRIMSON QUEEN: MARY TUDOR, D. M. Henderson, Duffield, 1933.

ELIZABETH, THE TUDOR PRINCESS, Marion King, Stokes, 1940.

HENRY VIII, Helen De G. Simpson, Appleton-Century, 1934.

A SHORT HISTORY OF THE ENGLISH PEOPLE, Vol. 2, J. R. Green, E. P. Dutton, 1915.

THE TOWER OF LONDON, William Harrison Ainsworth, E. P. Dutton, 1909.

FANFARE FOR ELIZABETH, Edith Sitwell, The Macmillan Company, 1946.

THE LIFE OF LADY JANE GREY, David W. Bartlett, Porter and Coates, 1887.

THE LILLY AND THE LEOPARDS, A. Harwood, Bobbs-Merrill, 1949.

THE SISTERS OF LADY JANE GREY, Richard Davey, Chapman & Hall Ltd., 1911.

THE NINE DAYS' QUEEN, Richard Davey, G. P. Putnam's Sons, 1909.

ABBEYS, CASTLES AND ANCIENT HALLS OF ENGLAND AND WALES, John Timbs and Alexander Gunn, Frederick Warne & Co., Ltd.

LIFE UNDER THE TUDORS, Edited by J. E. Morpurgo, Falcon Educational Books, 1950.

ABBEYS: THEIR RISE AND FALL, R. H. Malden, Oxford, 1944.

THE REIGN OF EDWARD VI, James Anthony Froude, E. P. Dutton, 1909.

COSTUME AND FASHION (THE TUDOR PERIOD), Volumes 1 and 2, Herbert Norris, E. P. Dutton, 1938.

LADY JANE GREY

Reluctant Queen

Chapter 1

A LEAF PRESSED IN A BOOK

A THRUSH, swaying on a low branch, lifted its head and sent music clear as a jet of fountain spray rising through the sun-spattered shadows. Then silence settled again over the garden at Sudeley Castle, the silence of autumn.

The girl sitting on a stone bench under the tree let her embroidery frame settle on her lap, her hands idle as she watched the bird. In her voluminous gown of black velvet with its full sleeves and pleated white lawn front or *barbe,* she looked sixteen or more. Her hair, except where it curved softly on her temples in tawny waves, was covered effectually by a French hood of black velvet. Against so much black her features stood out in startling relief, cameo-pure: the nose well shaped above a rather small, sensitive mouth; the brow low and broad; the eyes hazel, crystal-clear, and somehow, in their expression something questioning, something hesitant, as though much they had seen had left disturbing memories.

Though the hood, sweeping up and back from her brow, gave her added height, she was a tiny person, small boned, delicately formed. She was a wistful little figure there alone in the garden on that long ago autumn afternoon and the thrush eyed her, tilting its head inquisitively, possibly wondering what sort of creature it was who sat so quietly among her skeins of bright embroidery silk.

"Free—free you are, little bird, to fly where you will," the girl whispered, returning the bird's unblinking regard, "and whether or no your song pleases man's ear, still is your small head safe so long as your wings lift you beyond man's desire." Her lips curved in a half-smile as she watched the bird preen itself, watched it strip each feather carefully, then with a sudden bound soar up through the green canopy of leaves.

A leaf, dislodged by the flight, fluttered slowly down to land among the strands of silk spread out across the bench. The girl picked it up, held it a moment on her open palm, then on impulse slipped it between the pages of a small red book which she took from a silk reticule swinging at her belt.

I'll have it forever and ever to remember this, my last day at Sudeley, she thought. And suddenly the immobile young face with its too mature expression of serenity, crumpled, a spasm of sobbing shook the slender body and she broke into childish weeping.

Lady Jane Grey was eleven when Katherine Parr, Queen Dowager of England, died at Sudeley Castle on September 5, 1548. Thus did the lonely girl lose her best friend. On the nineteenth of September came the summons from her parents, the Marquis and Marchioness of Dorset, bidding her return at once to Bradgate, the Dorset family seat in Leicestershire to the north.

Sudeley Castle, the vast Gothic pile of buff-colored stone whose foundations had been laid in the eighth century, had become another home to Jane. Here there had been warmth and love and understanding; here there had been, recently at least, little talk of that monstrous thing which filled her whenever she heard it mentioned, with unfathomable terror: the Crown. The fear was partly instinctive, associated with bits of only half-understood conversations, rumors, reports. Her second cousins, Mary and Elizabeth and Edward Tudor were all a part of it—especially Edward. However, strangely enough, beloved Katherine Parr, the Queen, by her very proximity to the hated Thing, became paradoxically a buttress and a shield against it. With her, within sound of her quiet voice, Jane felt safe.

Now Katherine Parr was dead and the sense of security had vanished; now fear held her trapped. Tomorrow she would be on her way north. The Lady Frances, her mother, would greet her with habitual steely reserve: "You are grown blowzy with health, Jane. High time, indeed, that learning replaced time wasted in the daft pleasuring that ever has been the order at Sudeley." (Yet, forsooth, not a day at any castle where the Queen had been in residence had there been any shirking of study under good Master Coverdale. And why, if there had been naught but "daft pleasuring" at Sudeley had she, Jane, been kept there? Certainly it was at her parents' behest that she had been there at all.) Her father, if he chanced to be at home, would nod an absent-minded welcome.

Both the Dorsets were more often to be found with "a goodly companye" of friends hunting over the miles of forest and wasteland that comprised their sprawling estate. Jane would bite back the retort with which she longed to counter her mother's unreasonable criticism of her life at Sudeley. She would curtsy to both parents, then, followed by Mrs. Ellen and her maids, she would begin the draughty ascent to her rooms.

Sitting now in the mellow afternoon sunlight, her head resting against the tree, Jane resolutely dried her eyes and envisioned her sitting room at Bradgate. It was an enormous apartment with pillars and arches seeming to lift the darkness overhead as Atlas lifts the world. Narrow stained glass windows set high in the wall turned the perfumed rushes on the floor red and blue and gold, and in the great Norman fireplace a giant backlog whispered like a gossiping old woman. At the end of a massive table beside the hearth, arranged in an orderly row, a collection of books would be waiting: Greek, Latin, Hebrew, French, and Italian. At the other end a dulcimer and a lute. Ah, learning did, of a truth, wait.

Why should the Lady Frances have taken so accusing a tone to Jane when in her heart she must have known how unjust it was? Katharine, two years younger than Jane, was a scatterbrained romp who gave as little time to the efforts of her patient governess as she could; Mary, the crippled baby sister, was still in her cradle. Jane, the eldest daughter, was a tireless student and even at ten had been proficient in languages and philosophy. She played well on several instruments and her voice was true and wonderfully sweet. Why, then, should she have been the constant target for her mother's nagging exhortations to more and more and ever more work? True, there had been the necessary preparation for joining the Queen's household two years ago. After that—Did an unadmitted sense of guilt prod this blindly ambitious mother, rouse her to a reluctant awareness of motives she was loath to own? And being aroused, did she drive harder than she knew?

Desperately eager to leave Sudeley now, Jane found herself nevertheless thinking of the hours of concentrated work that surely awaited her at Bradgate. She thought of the nights when, after the tiny hammers with which she played the dulcimer had slid from her numb fingers and she swayed, half asleep, over the instrument, Mrs. Ellen (blessed Mrs. Ellen who had nursed her through her babyhood and would be her faithful friend to the end of her days) would rouse her.

"Come now, my lamb, Your Grace, there's still a half-hour before the practice time is ended. Try, lest my Lady Frances notice. Try—for Ellen. Come now—" Mrs. Ellen's voice was always low-pitched, her hands caressingly gentle as she twined the limp young fingers about the handles of the dulcimer sticks.

"But I want to sleep, Mrs. Ellen, just for a little while, please. Please. . . ." Drugged, helpless with weariness, Jane would lean against her. Oh, the bliss of sinking down, down into sleep, the agony of rousing herself to Mrs. Ellen's gentle shaking! She would have worked steadily since midafternoon and it was now long past midnight. The inhuman schedule of study made up by the Lady Frances lay on the table beside her. So many hours of Latin, Hebrew and Greek translation; so many hours of reading aloud in French and Italian; one spent in "cyphering;" two hours of music. A collation was to be served meanwhile "lest you grow over-weary and so blunt y'r thynking." Thus it was all written out in the Lady Frances's spidery hand.

This did not happen daily, but neither was it the exception. That Jane actually should have loved study in the face of such torment seems almost incredible. But both Roger Ascham, her tutor, and John Aylmer, her preceptor, agreed that as she grew older it was her greatest pleasure and favorite relaxation. To Ascham, however, she did admit in a moment of abject weariness:

"When I am in the presence of either father or mother, whether I speak, keep silence, . . . be sewing, playing . . . or doing anything else, I must do it . . . even so perfectly as God made the world, or else I am sharply taunted, so cruelly threatened that I think myself in hell till the time come that I must go to Mr. Aylmer who teacheth me so gently, so pleasantly, with such fair allurements to learning, that I think all the time nothing whilst I am with him."

John Aylmer it was who opened to little Lady Jane Grey the beauties of the Gospels. This good man, later to be the Bishop of London, taught the child her first prayers, prepared

her for her first Communion, opened her eyes and heart and mind to the beauties of the Christian faith. To Aylmer and to Ascham she owed much of the poise and strength of character that set her above all intrigue, all unworthiness at a time when a less lofty soul would have been tempted beyond strength to withstand.

Jane folded her work, got up and crossed the lawn of the little close formed by an angle in the wall surrounding that wing of the castle and by one side of the square tower in which her room at Sudeley was situated. She loved the tower wing and her room in it, adjoining the Queen's. Her window looked out across the gardens and the beautiful Cotswold Hills beyond. Here she could be quite alone when she chose; and now in her grief, it was a haven.

She reached the path and followed it between rows of pink and white gillyflowers and stock until she came to the low tower door which stood open. She entered, mounting the narrow stone steps, feeling the cold breath of the dark, ancient pile on her cheek, hearing the echo of her whispering footfalls on stone.

Just a week had passed since the death of the Queen . . . for she was the Queen Dowager though at the time of her death she had been the wife of the Lord High Admiral, Lord Seymour of Sudeley, the man she had loved long before Henry VIII had resolved she should be his wife, instead.

Jane heard Seymour's voice now echoing through one of the distant galleries as he spoke, probably, to Master Coverdale, and she entered her room and closed the door, shutting out the sound. Tomorrow she would be on her way to Bradgate in her uncomfortable, velvet-padded chariot. With the Queen gone, Sudeley was no longer the place she loved. She would be glad to leave it.

Chapter 2

BACKGROUND WITH FIGURES

HAD Lady Jane Grey's story been traced, step by dangerous step, back through the twisting shadows of time, one would have arrived at last at a sparkling morning in Plymouth almost fifty years earlier.

At last the voyage was over, praise God! The Princess Royal, Catalina, youngest daughter of King Ferdinand and Queen Isabella of Spain had arrived at Plymouth to become the bride of Arthur, Prince of Wales, son of England's King Henry VII.

The voyage had been long. Terrifying gales had lashed the top-heavy Spanish caravel one day; dead calm left it rolling on the oily swells the next, its sails limp, its royal passengers and its weary crew searching vainly for a breath of life-giving air. When air did come, it roared in with hurricane strength again, and in the inky darkness of the royal cabin the little ladies-in-waiting to Her Highness forgot etiquette and wept tears of sheer misery and terror. And Catalina, their royal mistress, reversing the normal procedure, comforted them.

She was not quite sixteen, this Spanish princess, and unlike her exquisite little ladies-in-waiting, she was pathetically plain. Her sturdy young body, instead of being girlishly rounded, was merely thick. Her blue eyes were a little prominent and too light for beauty; her mouth too firm, her chin too heavy. Her habitual expression was calm, unsmilingly thoughtful; and if the constant twittering, sparkling coquetry of her ladies annoyed her, this remarkable girl gave no sign.

From babyhood the Princess whom history would know as Catherine of Aragon, had been preparing herself for this marriage, perhaps for this stormy voyage. So, arrived at Plymouth, while the ladies and gentlemen of her suite wondered how they were to find strength to make even a presentable show, Catherine, glowing like the jewels she wore, settled herself more comfortably in her saddle and rode calmly, majestically toward Lambeth and her bridegroom.

However, scarcely five months after the marriage ceremony, after the processions and pageants, the masques and jousting, Prince Arthur sickened suddenly and died. Much political wrangling and religious debating buzzed about poor Catherine's head as the months, the years passed. Arthur's younger brother, Henry, was now Prince of Wales. He was a handsome, blue-eyed, golden-haired boy, strong willed, arrogant, yet deeply religious and something of a poet. He was twelve years old when he was formally betrothed to the eighteen-year-old Catherine and just eighteen himself when, newly crowned King, he married her.

At Court there was ugly whispering. What had the Bible to say about a man's marriage with the woman who had been his brother's wife? Was not such a marriage sinful? Would it be blest with children? And should it be, would they be weaklings? Mad? Touched, mayhap, by the white finger of leprosy?

One conviction the young monarch and his somber bride shared: the supreme importance of the dynasty. Catherine had entered into her marriage with the solemn hope of bearing sons to carry on the proud banner of the Tudors. Henry, gloriously young, alert to the dangers of enemies in the south, in Scotland to the north, saw in the Spanish girl a suitable mother for Tudor men, leaders, conquerors.

Henry was finding power a wonderful toy to play with. How dangerous a toy it was he probably did not suspect. At first he handled it dexterously, with care, but as the years passed he grew careless. Soon the only law he recognized was that of his own desire; his desire *was* the law and he brooked no opposition whatever. Marie, his beautiful sister to whom he was devoted, watched with a heavy heart and wondered where his arrogance was carrying him. One day Marie would be the grandmother of a little girl who would be named Jane Grey.

The Court of Henry VIII was the gayest, the most brilliant in all Europe. No entertainment was too lavish, no outlay of money too great. The young King gloried in impressing visiting ambassadors with the displays of his dazzling jewels, the heavy, solid gold details of even his simplest costumes and the trappings of his chargers. Catherine, shy, deeply religious, still speaking English brokenly, was alternately made much of by her husband and contemptuously ignored by him.

Early in the year 1516 a daughter was born to Catherine, a rosy, dimpled little girl with the dark, unwavering eyes of her Spanish ancestors and with her father's April nature. Mary Tudor, as she grew older smiled less, set her lips more firmly, but as a child she was full of chuckles and good spirits. Henry curbed his disappointment that she had not been a son and took great delight in carrying her about among his courtiers, encouraging her to prattle at them, convulsing them with her baby antics.

With the passing of time the young King began to lose his good looks. Much food and wine were making him gross, his great body unwieldy, his voice a hoarse rumble. Catherine, ailing now and stouter, paler, spent her days alternately in devotions and embroidering. That the Court was growing gayer, more abandoned, she knew; that Henry was pleasantly aware of her beautiful young ladies-in-waiting she could not help seeing. Among them was Anne Boleyn.

Anne Boleyn, ambitious, unscrupulous, and beautiful, had just returned from the Court of France where, like many girls of noble birth, she had been sent to learn the finer points of Court etiquette. She was just nineteen when Henry realized he was very much in love with her. Though she was deeply flattered, Anne was not easily won. She was too shrewd to be taken in either by the King's protestations or by her own admitted admiration for him. Well enough, she thought, for other silly young things to accept a monarch's attentions and then be discarded like a broken fan once His Majesty's interest cooled. For her part she would be Queen!

Henry, now determined to satisfy his conscience at all costs—for he was desperately afraid of any situation that showed him to himself in a bad light—cast about in his mind for some valid reason for divorcing Catherine. But how could he divorce her? She had been his wife for years, faithful, beloved by his people, respected by all the world.

Then out of the blue, Henry plucked his answer. The quotation from the Bible rang in his ears like a bell of freedom. He and Catherine never *had* been married! He had defied God by marrying Arthur's wife. Now it must end, this sinful marriage! He carried his case to Rome. Pope Clement sent emissaries to London to hear the case, and after much argument, after much weighing of evidence, the dispensation which would have given Henry his divorce and permitted him to marry Anne was refused. Catherine's simple, forthright plea as a good wife and mother had had its effect. Henry was stunned. Anne was beside herself with rage.

The Church, the clergy, had been falling into disrepute. Whereas in the past all ecclesiastical matters had been accepted as they were presented by the clergy to the laity, now restless students of religion were daring to ask questions. At Cambridge a priest, Thomas Cranmer, brilliant, clear-thinking, ruthless, went so far as to suggest that the universities should be invited to open discussion on the Papacy in general and its attitude toward the King's divorce in particular. Unrest was in the air and the authority of the Pope was being questioned.

Henry realized that most of the bishops of the realm owed their positions to him rather than to Rome and he knew that in a crisis they would follow him instead of the Pope. So Henry struck boldly. He assumed the title of Supreme Head of the Church in England, and under him as Archbishop of Canterbury, he appointed Thomas Cranmer.

He had married Anne Boleyn meanwhile, again because his "conscience" had warned him that he and Catherine were not married, never had been married. That by this reasoning he had placed the ugly word "illegitimate" opposite the name of Mary, did not apparently bother him. Perhaps never in history did a monarch succeed so well in rationalizing his own misdeeds. To Mary's already hypersensitive nature thus was added bitterness and quick spitefulness which one day would lash out with deadly accuracy at one innocent, her kinswoman, Jane Grey.

Though Henry VIII did become head of the Church in England, he was not responsible for the Reformation in England. The Great Religious Change was sweeping all Europe, not England alone. Henry Tudor simply used it as a means to get his divorce from Catherine. Most prominent figure in the English Reformation, he still was not its cause. His personal quarrel was solely with the Pope, not with the forms of

Catholic worship, many of which remained. The Mass, high and low, continued to be celebrated many times daily at the palace; the doctrine of Transubstantiation still held; fish was still the Friday dish. An era of confusion and martyrdom for countless innocents had been ushered in.

Catherine died on January 8, 1536. The King made no pretense of grief. The holiday gaieties were at their height. Three years earlier a daughter had been born to Anne and Henry and had been named Elizabeth. She was an engaging little minx with waving dark hair and enormous eyes, and Henry romped with her much as he had with her older half sister Mary, now seventeen.

The palace echoed with the rollicking sounds of mid-winter merriment; and for the first time Anne Boleyn wished the merriment might be curbed. She was Queen now, hated, scorned by all England, and she was discovering that just as her husband had smiled on her when she had been his wife's lady-in-waiting, so now he was finding one of her maids equally attractive. Her name was Jane Seymour.

Henry had squandered millions on jewels and cloth of gold to satisfy Anne's vanity and when rumors reached him that she was carrying on flirtations with some of his courtiers he acted quickly. Jane Seymour's star was rising. Anne was arrested, tried for treason, and beheaded on May 20, 1536.

In the palace at Chelsea, beyond the sound of the booming cannon which proclaimed the execution, the baby Elizabeth drowsed while Lady Bryane, her nurse, rocked her and sang:

I had a little nut tree,
Nothing would it bear
But a silver nutmeg
And a golden pear.

Henry and Jane Seymour were married in early June. The King was twice his bride's age and he found her youth and girlish deference much to his liking. However, he had reached middle age and was troubled by many things. A few years earlier he had lacerated his leg in a hunting accident. The wound refused to heal and caused him constant pain; Mary, Catherine's daughter, loyally refused to acknowledge that her mother's long marriage to the King had been unlawful; insurrections were sweeping the country. The temper and brutality of the King were finding new outlets. Then a gentling surprise stirred him to a semblance of good humor. Jane Seymour was to have a child.

On October 12, 1537 at Hampton Court the longed-for son was born. He was named Edward, this frail little boy who was carried in such state upon a velvet pillow beneath a canopy of gold to his baptism. His half sisters Mary, twenty now, thin-lipped and cynical, and Elizabeth, the three-year-old toddler who pranced and skipped under her heavy brocade, were in the procession to the font.

Mary smiled in bitter amusement, watching Anne Boleyn's little daughter throw her small body forward, tugging at the weight of her train borne by a nervous Court Lady. Meanwhile, at the castle the young mother, Jane Seymour, was

waging a losing battle with death. Her motto: "Bound to obey and to serve" had been richly redeemed. As quietly as she had appeared on the royal scene she now withdrew. Jane Seymour died on October 24, 1537 in the Catholic faith, and was buried at Windsor Castle.

In a gilded cradle in the wind-swept castle of Bradgate, Leicestershire, to the north, slept a baby girl, the first-born of the Marquis and Marchioness of Dorset. The Marchioness, Lady Frances, was the daughter of Marie, Duchess of Suffolk, sister of Henry VIII. Little Prince Edward was therefore second cousin to her baby daughter who had been named Jane for the young mother of the baby Edward. The children were just the same age, little Edward Tudor and his second cousin, Lady Jane Grey.

Princess Anne of Cleves, Henry's fourth bride, came from Germany. There was much about this gaunt, homely woman that must have touched the hearts of all thoughtful people. She had come to England under a misapprehension. The artist Holbein had been sent to Germany to paint her picture, and being an artist first and always, Holbein saw Anne of Cleves as a beautiful woman. The King was delighted with her portrait when it arrived, negotiations were quickly completed, and the future Queen set out for the country of her adoption. She was almost thirty-five, a spinster, unsought by any of the monarchs of her day. She was gentle and awkward with the awkwardness of the painfully shy, and being chosen the bride of the great Henry VIII must have seemed an incredible dream.

The King's Lord Privy Seal, the brutal Thomas Cromwell, had been instrumental in bringing about the approaching marriage, for Anne was Protestant and he saw the marriage as a strengthening link with all German Protestant royalty and nobility. A fanatical leader in the English Reformation, Cromwell had drawn heavily upon his imagination and had assured Henry that Anne of Cleves was a woman of great charm and beauty.

The King's bitter disappointment when finally he met his depressing bride-to-be cost Cromwell his head. The great Cromwell realized too late that the King's displeasure over Anne of Cleves, and the divorce he immediately demanded, would be a blow to the friendly Lutherans just as his divorce from Catherine had offended the Catholics. So Cromwell died.

Meanwhile Henry found his reason for divorcing Anne, and to him it seemed an excellent one: *he never had given his inward consent to the marriage!* He settled a magnificent fortune on the poor woman, established her in a palace, and spoke of her thereafter affectionately as "our dear sister." One cannot help wondering whether Anne's quiet acceptance of the divorce was due entirely to her lack of wits or to possession of more intelligence than she ever has been given credit for.

The death of Cromwell who for years had been the King's most faithful minister brought a shudder of horror to Catholics and Protestants alike, and men in high places spoke out frankly—too frankly for their own good. Immediately Henry made a law labeling all such critical speech a crime against high principle, and there followed a series of deaths by torture of the most inhuman sort.

A young woman at Hampton Court looked upon these ghastly deaths with unbelieving distaste. She was Katheryn Howard, the beautiful girl Henry had married the day of Cromwell's execution and within hours after his divorce from Anne of Cleves was granted. Katheryn had been one of the ladies-in-waiting appointed to Anne. She was a slip of a girl, just eighteen, tiny, hazel-eyed, plump and dimpled. The King, nearing fifty, longing for the company of youth and for gaiety, had fallen deeply in love with her.

Unfortunately pretty little Katheryn had many of the tendencies which had brought her equally pretty cousin, Anne Boleyn, to her death years earlier. Katheryn was a little wanton without scruples or standards of behavior. So it was inevitable that her many brazen escapades should eventually reach the ears of the King. Katheryn Howard, unable to the last to believe that she actually was to die for her flirtations, was beheaded in February, 1542. And for no Queen, it was said, did Henry VIII grieve as he did for the unprincipled little Katheryn who betrayed him and ridiculed the love he lavished upon her.

But the King was growing old and he was a sick man. His judgment was bad; his memory played him tricks; his leg ulceration was causing him constant pain. This unwieldy tyrant with the lives of so many martyrs on his conscience was suddenly lonely and afraid. Like a small boy, he wanted someone to talk to; someone to share the fireside; to listen sympathetically when he described his endless aches and pains; someone to grow old with him. What comfort were all his sergeants and yeomen? His chaplains and subchaplains, virginal players, cupbearers and servers? He wanted a wife.

But where to choose? Henry's temper had become so vile, his condemnation so lightning-swift that even his most trusted servitors dreaded crossing his path. No sane woman voluntarily would have chosen to find favor with him. Sooner or later on some trumped-up charge she was bound to die by his command. Yet, eighteen months after the execution of Katheryn Howard, Katherine Parr became the sixth and last wife of Henry VIII. And it was in the company of lovely Katherine Parr that Lady Jane Grey first came to Court.

Chapter 3

THE QUEEN'S HOUSEHOLD

THE Lady Frances, Marchioness of Dorset, would have been a strikingly beautiful woman had it not been for the expression of steely cold indifference which gave to her face a peculiarly masklike quality. In conversation with her one had the baffling sensation of being unseen and unheard as my lady looked through and beyond one. She was an overbearingly proud woman, the Lady Frances, niece of His Majesty's Grace, King Henry. That her husband was rated one of the wealthiest noblemen in the realm, though one of the dullest, may have had some bearing on her own shortcomings. That she counted among her few close friends the gentle Lady Latimer, daughter of Sir Thomas Parr, was to her credit.

Katherine Parr, before she was fourteen, had been married to Lord Borough of Gainsborough, Yorkshire, a man so very much older than she that she called one of his daughters by a former marriage "little Mother." Two years later, following

Lord Borough's death, Katherine again married and this time another nobleman of great wealth, Lord Latimer. Latimer was a staunch Catholic; Katherine, who was educated far beyond the limits of most women of her day, was an ardent student of what was popularly known as the New Learning. Protestantism as such was actually unknown in its various forms since the word "Protestantism" had not yet been coined.

After Lord Latimer's death, when Katherine was about thirty-two, her London house became the gathering place for scholars, searchers after religious truths, students of the New Learning. Among them was the Lady Frances who was neither searcher nor scholar—the Marchioness excelled in archery and horsemanship—but whose interest in anything which was an offshoot of the Reformation was absorbing. So the two women had become close friends.

On a spring afternoon Katherine Parr sat on the terrace of Dorset Place, the Dorset London town house, chatting with the Lady Frances. The day was warm; sparrows twittered and scolded in the ivy that covered the garden wall; on a lower level of the terrace two little girls tossed a beanbag slowly back and forth, their movements stiff, doll-like, hampered as they were by the heavy, constricting brocades and starched ruches which hemmed them in.

Two nurses sat knitting on a bench nearby. Suddenly the younger child threw the beanbag to the ground and ran to hide her face in her nurse's lap. Little Lady Katharine Grey was hot and tired. Her sister retrieved the bag, stood for a moment with it in her hand, then began climbing the broad shallow steps to the upper terrace.

Mrs. Ellen, her nurse, started after her, but Jane waved her back. "Nay, Mrs. Ellen, hinder me not," she begged. "I'd speak with Her Grace, the Lady Katherine." And the little girl, lifting her heavy skirts carefully, continued to trudge up the steps.

Katherine Parr was smiling, shaking her head as she addressed the Lady Frances, apparently answering a question that just had been asked.

"Aye, an' it can be duly arranged, His Majesty's health permitting, we'll be wed sometime in July. We. . . ."

"But Katherine," the Lady Frances's voice held a note of real concern, "do you know—surely you must—how grave a task you undertake? His Majesty, my uncle, since the shameless little Howard's betrayal of his devotion, is sick in mind as well as body. A thoughtless word, a smile ill begotten, and the rack or the torch might well follow. My own head, forsooth, could fall for such light chatter were it known. But we're friends, Katherine, and I'd have you think well before it is too late."

But Katherine only shook her head anew. "Nay, Frances," she said quietly, "I've no fear, none in the least degree. I'll care for His Majesty's Grace, I'll be the wife he'd have me, and the years will be kind and England prosper. Ah, and here," she smiled winsomely and held out her hand, "here, methinks is a sweet little maid for my household. Jane, sweetheart, come hither."

The Lady Frances had flushed with annoyance when first she spied Jane standing hesitantly near her guest's chair. Where *was* Mrs. Ellen? After all, Jane had her own household, yet here she was like any guardsman's child, simpering at Katherine Parr's elbow! Then the Marchioness's brow cleared. What was Katherine saying? Hadn't she called Jane a "sweet little maid for my household?" When she became Queen that meant Jane, with possibly one other child or three others to make the number even, would walk before her in processions; would light her to bed, long tapers held high in their small hands as they followed the winding galleries of Hampton Court, Nonesuch, Windsor, Oatlands, Greenwich, and other places where the Queen of England might be in residence.

The Lady Frances watched as her daughter moved closer to Katherine Parr, put her tiny hand in the lady's long, slender one, and smiled up at her with the unabashed adoration of a lonely, sensitive child who is lovingly spoken to. The mother's chaotic thinking had blocked out the conversation between the woman and child opposite her, but Jane's expression and her happily bobbing head as Katherine spoke conveyed a story, clear, unqualified: Jane's future was established, assured. She would automatically become part of the vast Tudor assemblage. Great-niece of the King, Princess of the Blood, once she became a member of the Queen's household a crown was certain to follow. Queen Jane—like the gentle Queen, Jane Seymour for whom she had been named. Here was good fortune. Here was a dream realized with unexpected suddenness.

The Lady Frances composed her features and cleared her throat. "As to what we lately discussed, Katherine," she said, trying to sound casual, "you know I wish you well, albeit my conscience bids me warn you. As to Jane, here. She's still a babe, but not too young to learn those things which a Princess should know to render her pleasing in exalted places. An' you want her, say a year hence, you'll find her docile and well trained. Jane—" she waved her hand in curt dismissal—"do you return to your sister and Mrs. Ellen. Methinks Mrs. Ellen is become witless to let you come up here. Be gone—quickly!"

Jane hesitated another instant, her glance traveling from her mother to Katherine Parr and back again. "Mother, Your Grace," she began, kneading the beanbag nervously between her two hands, "an' Her Grace, the Lady Latimer would have me now, could—could I—"

"Mercy upon us, no! Be gone, I say! No, Katherine," as her guest murmured a quick assent, "though you are soon to be my gracious Queen, yet must I refuse you this. What's come over the child to be thus overbold? Where's Mrs. Ellen?"

Mrs. Ellen was deep in conversation with her beloved nursling who just had rejoined her, her eyes shining, her cheeks scarlet.

"Didst hear, Mrs. Ellen?" Jane gave a happy skip as they walked back along the pebbled path to the nursery wing. "Didst hear how I'm to be of the Lady Katherine's household?"

Mrs. Ellen settled her bonnet more comfortably. "Well, now, and isn't that pleasant, indeed? Methinks, though, the

Lady Katherine hath household enow without taking my wee Jane." She smiled down at the little girl. "When said she this, sweetling?"

"Oh, a moment gone. Her Grace, my mother, did say the Lady Katherine would be Queen—'my gracious Queen' she called her—and that I would be docile and well trained. Thus she said *exactly,* Mrs. Ellen. I'm going to my Lady Katherine's!"

The nurse stopped stock still and the color drained slowly from her face. Then, "Surely Her Grace spoke in jest," she answered. "Besides, an' she spoke truly, it would still be one or two years before you would be of proper age to act as attendant to a Queen. Let's think no more about it, my Jane. Furthermore, you are a Princess of the Blood, thus you *could* not wait upon the Queen. Put it from your thoughts, child."

But Jane's mind was made up. "Not wait on her, mayhap, Mrs. Ellen, but be with her and carry her candle and thread her needle and—and—"

"So be it, so be it, but not today nor tomorrow nor a year of tomorrows. Now let us see what there is for supper."

Jane, however, was not interested in supper. Lonely, wanting affection which her mother seemed incapable of feeling for anyone or anything, Jane had given her heart to the Lady Latimer when they first had met months earlier. Then Katherine had smiled, patted her cheek, called her "dear child." To the love-starved little girl the gesture and the endearment were accolade. The Lady Latimer became a combined fairy godmother and an angel straight down from one of the stained glass windows in the Bradgate chapel.

To see the Latimer sedan carriers turn in at the gates of Dorset Place was enough to send Jane running to Mrs. Ellen or one of the undernurses. "The Lady Latimer is here!" she would sing out blithely. "Come, please, an' we make haste we may greet her before she goes in to my mother! Hurry, please!" She would tug the hand nearest her.

Her request was seldom granted. So today had been like a sliver of white light cutting through dungeon blackness. To be a member of the beloved Lady Katherine's household! The child's imagination flew ahead to a realm of such happiness as only a lonely six-year-old Princess could invent. Her cheeks blazed; usually reticent, Jane chattered like one of the captive-magpies in the Bradgate aviary.

She was going to the Lady Latimer's . . . . For how long? Well, no one knew, exactly. When? As soon, forsooth, as she was perfect in the lessons she was to be taught. Oh, it would be very soon, make no doubt. So she chattered on to Mrs. Ellen; to her sister who looked up from her doll only long enough to nod politely at first and later to observe, "Janie talk too much"; to the undernurses and tirewomen and in the hearing of pages.

One of these it was who tossed his handsome head laughingly and addressed the women: "Methinks the Lady Jane knows not that a pretty head must be screwed on wondrous tight at Court if 'tis to keep to the neck it fits. On goes the crown, off goes the head." He chuckled at his own wit.

The women frowned and one spoke, lowering her voice. "Sh! Watch thy tongue, thou empty-headed donkey! Her Grace knows nought of Hampton Court nor any other royal household. God send she never will."

But Jane had heard. "His Majesty's Grace, the King, dwells much at Hampton Court, that I know. But it is not there the Lady Latimer will have her household, I'm sure. She will be Queen and—and—she will have her own palace, all her own. And there I will be!" Urgency tinged her voice now and the women exchanged uneasy glances.

This small moment out of time, with its banter and happy childish boasting, held the first tangible contribution to Jane's fear of queenship. She may have forgotten the actual incident, the words, but the susceptible young brain had caught the full impact and the scar remained.

On July 12, 1543, Katherine Parr and Henry VIII were quietly married in one of the chapels at Hampton Court. If the bride had any misgivings on her honeymoon as she watched the terrible, chameleonlike changes that transformed her bridegroom from a genial fat man, full of laughter and amusing anecdotes one moment to a thin-lipped, murderous fanatic the next, she made no sign. What she thought of the burning of three innocent men accused of heresy a month after her wedding, history does not say. She was learning that "to be the wife he'd have me" called for all the tact and bravery she could muster.

One thing she did quietly and fearlessly: she brought Princess Mary, now a bitter woman of twenty-seven and Princess Elizabeth, thirteen, to Hampton Court for long visits. To little Prince Edward, six, whose household was formally established at Hatfield, she gave a tender devotion; and in return he adored her.

Meanwhile, at Bradgate little Jane's schooling to make her "docile and well trained" had begun in earnest. French, Latin, Greek, these replaced the delicately carved and painted wooden dolls, the beanbags, and hoops. The tiny fingers must come down firmly, yet softly withal, upon the virginal keys. In slightly less than two years Jane's summons came, a charmingly worded invitation, which was a royal command.

Her cheeks pinker than usual with excitement, Jane rode pillion before a yeoman upon an enormous, richly caparisoned charger. Her curls splayed out from under her tiny velvet riding cap with its graceful plume, and because she was a Princess of the Blood, going abroad for all the populace to gaze upon if they so minded, a little velvet mask covered the upper part of her face. Through its slits her hazel eyes sparkled like polished amber. A small blue velvet cape embroidered in gold fluttered about her shoulders; and as she was "riding" and so must wear the full complement of an equestrienne's habit, her hands must be encased in heavily embroidered gauntlets of white leather.

Before and behind her rode two armed guardsmen in the Dorset livery; then Mrs. Ellen and the new governess, Mrs. Ashley, on sedate, carefully stepping palfries; and bringing up in the rear the carts bearing luggage. It was an impressive cavalcade that wound through London Town and along the river from Dorset Place to Greenwich that spring morning.

Busy housewives stopped their dusting to watch it pass; flower vendors and lowly packmen flattened themselves against walls to escape the prancing hoofs of the guardsmen's mounts; a traveling showman with his trained bear ran for cover in an angle between buildings. Royalty passes by! Make way! Make way!

Jane leaned comfortably in the crook of the yeoman's arm. Cool sunshine spread a golden haze over the morning; a breeze smelling of distant farm lands, lifted the town's stale mustiness and set Jane's plume dancing. She laughed aloud in sheer well-being and turned to speak to the yeoman, when there was a disturbance in the road ahead.

She caught her breath. With one hand she pointed, with the other she clutched at the rein, and the horse plunged. The horseman quieted it and smiled down at Jane.

"What is it, my lady?"

"Look! Oh, do look! What are they doing to those men? Please stop!"

Coming toward them were two men in rags, filthy, ashen-faced. Mere shells of humanity, skeletons, they stumbled along, hampered by the heavy chains that bound them together and to the soldiers leading them. Almost abreast of the cavalcade bound for Greenwich, the soldiers, cursing, flung them to the side of the road. One of the prisoners broke into

a whimpering cry and briefly stretched out his hand. Then the cavalcade swept by and the miserable scene was gone.

Frantically Jane leaned out, straining to look back. "Oh, please do stop!" she pleaded. "They're hurting those men! Didn't you see? Please!"

But the yeoman pressed her gently back. "No, my lady, there's nought we can do," he answered. "Offenders against our gracious King deserve punishment. Offense against the Crown merits death. Pray, think no more on it." He gave the reins a slight tug and the horse's pace quickened.

In sudden terror Jane turned her head up and back to look into the rugged, bearded face of the yeoman. "Mrs. Ellen—she's there, behind us? Art certain?" She had to know she was not alone. Something said—was it two years ago, and where? And who said it? A page mayhap? That something came swimming back through memory now like a hideous, dark, thick sea snake gliding through clear water: the Crown—that was it—the Crown.

The sunshine had gone out of the morning. Jane closed her eyes to hold in the tears of fright that threatened to slide down under the pretty mask and mark her for a cry baby and a coward.

"Yes, my lady, Mrs. Ellen rides directly behind us," the yeoman answered in the tone he probably used to his own children when they asked strange questions.

Mrs. Ellen was there. She would always be there. So, reassured, Lady Jane Grey rode toward Greenwich.

Chapter 4

THE KING IS DEAD! LONG LIVE THE KING!

JANE had not been long at Court before, with the unfailing instinct of childhood, she separated the true from the false among the swarms of bejeweled courtiers who comprised its personnel. She tried never to come within speaking distance of the Lord Chancellor Wriothesley—she could not have said why. His slow, suave smile, his habit of continually wringing his white, large-knuckled hands filled her with a distaste she did not understand.

Nor did she trust Sir Thomas Seymour, the popular, handsome Court favorite. His unchanging good humor, his too ready laughter, somehow struck a false note. Jane had the uncomfortable feeling that he might suddenly point at her and go into one of his characteristic gales of laughter over something about her that amused him. Naturally, Sir Thomas never did; in fact, Sir Thomas probably was not aware of Lady Jane Grey at any time during her first year at Court. Nevertheless, the feeling persisted.

But it was the dark-visaged Earl of Warwick, later to be created Duke of Northumberland whom she feared as something cold, deadly. Jane had only to hear his voice in the antechamber to send her hurrying in the opposite direction on some real or fabricated errand for the Queen. Once she heard him upbraid a page before a roomful of people. She never saw the page again and could not bring herself to ask what had become of him; but from that day the very name Warwick struck dread to her heart.

There were others, though, first at Greenwich and then at Hampton Court whom she loved. Doctor Wendy, the Queen's physician, for instance, and most of all Will Somers, the King's fool. Somers was not a romantic figure like the famous Triboulet of an earlier era in France, nor had he the crafty shrewdness of Archie Armstrong, jester to James I. Jane thought Will Somers the kindest man in the whole world. The occasion which brought him, like a strong hand lifting her out of a pit, was one she never was able to erase from her memory.

It was a summer day, close and humid, and a storm that had been threatening since morning, moved nearer. The palace had been very quiet all day and Jane found the Queen for once short-tempered, taciturn. As the afternoon wore on she made another effort to cheer Her Majesty. She never had seen her royal mistress quite like this, pale to the point of being haggard, her fingers twisting nervously in her lap as she sat having her hair dressed, her answers to questions put to her by her ladies short, absent-minded. Finally she had curled up on a couch in her dressing room, her eyes on the lowering sky stretching away toward London.

Jane had learned to play accompaniments on the lute to several ballads and the Queen encouraged her to sing whenever she would. So now the small lute with its fluttering ribbons was taken from its velvet case to rest on Jane's lap as she sat beside the Queen's couch and sang Sir Thomas Wyatt's ballad of admonition.

> Forget not yet the tried intent
> of such a truth as I have meant;
> (the sweet, childish treble sang)
> My great travail so gladly spent,
> Forget not yet!
>
> Forget not! O, forget not this!—
> How long ago hath been and is,
> The mind that never meant amiss—
> Forget not yet!

Jane shifted the lute and caught a quick glimpse of the Queen. She was lying back, one arm thrown across her eyes, her lower lip caught between her teeth, her whole bearing tense.

> Forget not then thine own approved
> The which so long hath thee so loved,
> Whose steadfast faith yet never moved:
> Forget not this!

The song ended on a minor note. Katherine reached out and touched Jane's hand. "No more, sweet. Run along . . ." and as Jane hesitated ". . . run along quickly. Find Mrs. Ashley—mayhap it will not storm—thy pony—a ride in the park—but go, please, quickly." She waved impatiently, her eyes still covered by her upflung arm, and Jane felt she was close to tears.

"Yes, Your Majesty, I go." She put down the lute and tiptoed from the room, thankful as she was so often that she was the only girl in the Queen's household. Another girl might have insisted on staying, not recognizing her mistress's need for solitude. Jane had just reached the corridor leading to her own apartments, her thoughts still on the Queen, when a series of explosions coming from the direction of London halted her, spun her around as though from the great windows facing toward the city she would surely see some evidence of what had caused the blast.

She stood very still, her eyes wide with terror, her hands pressed convulsively over her mouth. She saw a lackey hurrying along far down the corridor stop and cross himself. Then he disappeared and she was standing alone in the shadows when a second thunderous roar set the very windows rattling. The silence that followed had an almost tactile quality, a dimension that grew in nightmare volume until the terrified girl longed to tear it with her fingers and through the ripped aperture escape into safe reality. The dim, high-vaulted corridor was an evil dream world and she the only living being in it. Sobs began crowding her chest, threatening to suffocate her.

"Jesu . . . Jesu . . ." she whispered, and began running blindly.

Then two strong arms reached out from the shadows and Jane found herself held secure amid a tinkle of small bells and the rustle of silk. The impact made her gasp and instinctively she closed her eyes. When she opened them she looked into the kind dark eyes of Will Somers, the jester.

"Lady Jane, Your Grace," he began, releasing her yet steadying her with a hand on each elbow. The bells on his cap and around his wrists whispered with her trembling.

"Oh, Will—Will Somers," her voice was barely audible, "what is it? All London must be in ashes. Are we invaded?"

"No, my lady, there's nought to be afrighted of," he answered. "I must not tarry lest His Majesty call me and find me absent. Only this, and pray attend me well: let Her Majesty, the Queen, take all possible care. What we heard this moment gone was exploding gunpowder . . . ."

"Gunpowder?"

"Aye, this day was Mistress Anne Askew of Leicestershire burned after the rack. Gunpowder did but shorten her agony."

"Mistress Askew? Burned? And the rack? Oh, Will Somers, in mercy, *why?*"

The jester shrugged and looked into space and the muscles of his cheek twitched against the tight band that fastened his cap. " 'Twas said she did dispute over much concerning some things in the New Testament and did scoff at the Mass," he answered after a pause. "She is—was, I know—an acquaintance of Her Majesty's and came ofttimes to Her Majesty's bower with other learned ladies. Now 'tis whispered that His Grace, Bishop Gardiner of Winchester and the Lord Chancellor Wriothesley feel sure they have a case—the charge heresy—against Her Majesty. . . ."

"Not the Queen, Somers! Not Queen Katherine!"

"Yes, my lady. But there is yet hope, even though the King hath already signed the warrant calling for. . . ."

A page, flushed and panting, bowed briefly as he halted beside them. "Will—Will Somers," he stuttered, trying vainly to steady his breathing, "make all haste. His Majesty's Grace calls for you—he's in a great state. For thy soul's sake, and mine, since I was sent to find thee, stir thyself! Pardon, Lady Jane . . . ."

Somers looked steadily at Jane, not trusting himself to say more before the page, willing her to remember exactly what he had said and to do what she could to warn the Queen. Then he nodded to the boy, and Jane watched them go running through the half-light and disappear.

Rain lashed at the windows, thunder rumbled. Jane knew Mrs. Ellen and Mrs. Ashley were in their rooms, believing she was with the Queen. But what had they thought of the explosions, more horrible now that she knew their cause? Or had they known as Will Somers had known? And what had Will Somers said? Katherine, the Queen, was under suspicion, with Gardiner and Wriothesley her accusers.

Anne Askew—Jane remembered her so well, brown-eyed, vivacious, earnest in her frank disavowal of certain accepted tenets of the Church following the Reformation. Half an hour ago Anne Askew had died at the stake after being broken on the rack, as a heretic, for conscience's sake. Jane recalled Queen Katherine's grave attention to Anne Askew's spirited attacks upon many of the existing abuses of religious practice. And for this the Queen was accused—of what? And if not cleared, what had Somers hinted? That the King already had signed her death warrant? But this was unthinkable! She must have help . . . but where find it?

For an instant Jane thought her imagination was playing her tricks, then she heard it again, a cry, low, heartbroken, despairing, coming from the Queen's apartments. Was the whole world going mad? Jane put her hands over her ears. Ten years of age, old beyond her years, acquainted now, after more than a year at Court, with the unpredictable vagaries of a sick monarch, nevertheless she could not face the hideous possibility which she just had learned might touch one to whom she gave a daughter's love. The sound came again, long drawn, blood-chilling. Jane lifted her skirts and ran as fast as their great weight would permit, back to the Queen's apartments. As she reached the door, it burst open and a serving woman, wringing her hands, her eyes dark with compassion, stepped quickly into the corridor.

"Oh, my lady," she whispered, "please, for mercy's sake, fetch Doctor Wendy! Her Grace, the Queen, is like to go mad with fright. She's just had a message saying His Majesty hath

signed a document saying she is to go to the stake for heresy!"

No! No! The words burned into her brain like acid. Doctor Wendy, of course. He would know what to do. But the King! Jane turned—and stopped. Approaching from the King's wing, came a strange procession. Four giant men carried between them a vast thronelike chair, a sort of sedile, upon which sat the velvet-and-fur clad figure of the King. Before it minced Will Somers, head wagging, coxcomb beating time to his gait, bells tinkling.

Jane watched the approaching group with a mixture of dread and almost hysterical relief. The serving woman withdrew, leaving the girl alone, silhouetted in the lighted doorway. She sank to her knees. Behind her the weeping continued.

"Your Majesty's Grace, my liege . . . ." Her small hands clasped, she faced the King.

At a sign from him, the chair was set down. Henry leaned forward, his small eyes blazing in their yeasty pockets of flesh. In spite of the oppressive heat, he was wearing a surcoat of wallflower-red velvet, lined with sable and heavily embroidered in gold. His shapeless fat hands blazed with jewels, and on his massive head a black velvet hat, feather-trimmed. A fine silken hose was drawn over one leg; the other, stretched stiffly before him, was swathed in bandages. Perspiration poured down his cheeks and matted the fur on the collar of his surcoat.

With a waggling finger he motioned to the kneeling girl. "Get up, get up, Jane Grey," he commanded, "and come here . . . *here!*" He pounded his silk-clad knee. One of the bearers stepped forward and Jane felt herself lifted and placed gently on the King's lap. Gingerly, rigid, she tried to face her great-uncle and encountered fur that smelled of camphor and bergamot. A heavy jeweled pendant, swinging against the King's broad chest, rubbed the back of her neck, a shaking hand rested on her shoulder.

"Hmph, thou'rt a sweet maid, little Jane, a Tudor through and through," spoke a wheezing voice. "Come, take us to the Queen who weeps. We like not the sound, do we?"

He patted her hand and Jane, squirming around to look up at him, finally succeeded and found the King smiling at her. "No, Sire," she answered, and tried to match the royal smile with one as friendly, "we like it not. Your Majesty's Grace alone can comfort her."

Had she said too much? Jane held her breath, then expelled it slowly in relief when a rumbling chuckle and another series of unsteady pats on her hand reassured her. She was lifted down again and while she, remembering etiquette, bowed her way from the royal presence, the chair was moved through the doorway. The bearers withdrew, the doors closed, the weeping ceased.

Just what words were spoken by the desperate, quick-thinking Queen Jane never knew, but through the days that followed, Katherine's cleverness in proving her innocence to the King became a favorite topic in the palace. Of this Jane heard nothing. However, on the afternoon following she did see the humiliation of those who had plotted Katherine's death.

His Majesty, leaning on the Queen's arm, walked slowly, painfully, in the garden. He was in high good humor, calling the Queen "Kate, sweetheart," pointing out this flower, that butterfly; jesting with Lady Herbert, the Queen's sister; tweaking Jane's curls. The day was gloriously cool after yesterday's rain. Away with thoughts of torture and tears. Then, what. . .? His Majesty squinted into the sunlight, not believing what he saw.

Marching toward him in full regalia, came Wriothesley and Gardiner and forty of the guard to arrest the Queen! The King had forgotten the warrant he had signed only a few days earlier!

Furiously he faced the bewildered Chancellor and Bishop. "Knaves! Fools! Shameless beasts!" he hurled at them. "Out of our sight and never return!" Then, as the company got itself out of the palace grounds with all possible speed and what dignity it could maintain, he again linked his arm in Katherine's.

By how slight a margin had she escaped! Looking at the swallows wheeling against the blue summer sky, did Jane wonder how freedom like theirs would seem? What went on in the active mind of the sixteenth-century girl moving deeper and ever deeper into the web of intrigue floating like a mist about her?

Peace was restored and the Court prepared for a visit from the French envoy, Monsieur d'Annebault. The royal family and its households moved to Hampton Court, and for the first time young Prince Edward, acting as heir apparent, rode in his father's place to London to greet a visitor. The ten-year-old Princeling, clad in cloth of gold, sat his pony with easy grace, and Jane, watching with other ladies from a window high above the courtyard, turned impulsively to Lady Herbert.

"Methinks His Highness rideth with a stout heart, say you not so, Madam?" she asked smiling.

Lady Herbert snapped shut the little blue enamel perfume ball she was sniffing and nodded. "Aye, God keep him, he hath a stout heart and a truly fair spirit—pure, unselfish, rarely sweet. What a comfort to his royal father!"

That evening and for many succeeding evenings the great hall at Hampton Court rang with festivities. Balls, games of chance, theatricals, feasts, these filled the palace from dusk to sunrise. Jane danced with Prince Edward and found him a strange combination of arrogance and timidity. Because he was her relative and exactly her own age, she bit her lip to keep from giggling when he narrowly missed throwing himself off his feet as he swept too impressive a bow before little Anne Seymour. Yet, when he led Jane off gravely in the steps of the *galliard* he was all little boy.

"His Majesty, my father, watcheth me," he confessed miserably, counting steps, "and this dance maketh me loutish as a mutton. Forgive me, Cousin, an' I tread upon thy toes." And Jane smiled into his eyes and assured him his dancing was perfect. Edward might be a strange boy, but she liked him.

Those were the last sumptuous festivities of the reign of

Henry VIII. The days of the King were drawing to a close. As summer waned, his indomitable will to conquer pain and disease faltered. He kept to his bed, that enormous structure at Whitehall, so high on its dais that one prelate looking at it with its priceless gold hangings, declared it looked like a High Altar.

Christmas came and the young Prince thanked his father for a gift and then, manfully winking back the tears, was led away. There was some pretense of holiday gaiety; minstrels played and sang softly just outside the sickroom door; Princess Mary, trying to hide her grief, stood a moment beside the bed to receive her father's blessing. Katherine knelt, Henry's feverish hand against her cheek. He called her his "good and true spouse," reminding her that he had made generous provision for her in his will.

Princess Elizabeth, fourteen, and Edward ten, were not there after Christmas. Elizabeth probably was with her household in the palace at Enfield, Edward at Hertford. As for Lady Jane Grey, undoubtedly she was at Whitehall. The King was fond of her—wasn't she his favorite sister's grandchild?—and there must have been times when the sick man called for "Dorset's child, the little Jane." Such a time came on an evening shortly before he died, and a page was sent to bring her to the sickroom.

Smiling fixedly as she had been taught, Jane mounted the broad, shallow steps to the bed. She must not waver, she must not cry out or grow faint at what she saw. The mountain of unrecognizable, livid flesh propped among the pillows must be His Majesty, so you made sure you kept your mind on that.

Gasping for breath in the foul air, Jane curtsied. A thick mumble came from the bed. In a panic, Jane realized she could not understand a word of it. A quiet voice spoke in her ear. "The King asks if Your Grace had a happy Christmas," said Will Somers.

"Aye, my liege, Your Majesty." Jane spoke clearly and made herself smile into the bloodshot eyes and move closer as a finger beckoned feebly. "Indeed, an' Your Majesty had been with us at the merrymaking, it would have been perfect. God send you abundant good health soon," she added in a spurt of pity, and was rewarded by a nod from the sick King and another mumbled exhortation which Somers translated.

"His Majesty said, 'Well spoken, little maid. Even now we feel strengthened by your good wish.' Best go now, my lady. His strength fails."

So stepping carefully, Jane backed from the dais and from the dreadful chamber. At the door, looking back, she caught a last glimpse of the vast, elevated bed in its dim aura of candlelight. Above it, surmounting its canopy, the Crown . . . the Crown.

In the early morning of January 28, 1547, with Archbishop Cranmer, hearing his final words, Henry VIII, King of England, died.

So passed a monarch known best for his monstrous crimes of inhumanity. Nevertheless England owed much to Henry VIII. He was a liberal patron of the arts; through him the great British Navy was organized; and he it was who made of Parliament a practical, working body. The fabric of his life pattern, though coarse and ill-woven, embodied a strength and a resilience which inevitably drew England several degrees up the steep slopes of human progress.

Chapter 5

UNWELCOME SURPRISE

JANE drew her satin-lined hood more closely about her head and wrapped her cape tighter. Hanworth, Katherine's dower house in Middlesex, had been reached only after a cold, windy journey. Now the March twilight, full of moving blue shadows, was closing in and the thought of firelight and warmth was welcome.

Funny, she mused, watching the trees bend in black silhouette against the fading pink of the sunset, the last time I came to be with Her Grace it was morning—and I wore my blue cape—and I was afraid in one special way. Now it's evening and I'm cold, and my way of being afraid is—is different, but still part of the other fear. Why did Thomas Seymour come to Bradgate—only now he is the Lord High Admiral, Baron of Sudeley— Why? Why did he?

Mrs. Ellen and Mrs. Ashley had gone to another entrance. Jane stood alone beside Lord Sudeley in the wind, waiting for the door to open, hating his gauntleted hand on her shoulder, pretending not to hear as he leaned to ask, "Cold, Lady Jane? Upon my soul, you're shivering." He moved to throw his cloak about her, but at that moment the door was flung open.

"The Queen's Grace attends you in the solar, my lord, Your Grace." The lackey deftly caught Sudeley's tossed gloves and plumed hat and cloak as they were flung at him, and motioned down the gallery.

Her full cape billowing out behind her, Jane kept pace with the Lord Admiral's long stride, and turned at last into a large room lighted by tapers and a great fire blazing on the hearth.

"Jane! Dearest child!" From the dancing shadows beside the hearth, the black-clad figure of the Queen Dowager detached itself. Jane ran forward and was wrapped in a warm embrace that smelled faintly of rose and verbena.

"Oh, Lady—Your Grace!" She clung happily, breathing in the peace and sweet security Katherine's presence always gave her.

The Queen disengaged her gently, pushing back her hood. This child with her great hazel eyes and skin like a flower petal, was growing up. Dorset, her father, was wiser than one gave him credit for to let her join the Court circle again .... Must ask Sudeley all about how it happened. Aloud she said, " 'Tis wondrous good to have you here again, dear. Look, we're a family circle ...."

Jane stole a glance about and from the shadows familiar

faces stood out, faces she had known during her two years at Court, before the death of the King. There were the Herberts, and Lord and Lady Fitzwilliam, and—Jane caught her breath. There, leaning against one of the marble pilasters of the great carved mantel, stood the Princess Elizabeth. She must have known what a dramatic picture she made, standing there in the ruddy glow of the fire, a slim, graceful figure clad in cherry velvet, one hand resting on the head of a giant mastiff, the other behind her, tracing the length of the pilaster.

Elizabeth's hair was popularly described as auburn or red. It was, as a matter of fact, as ebony black as her mother, Anne Boleyn's had been, waving in thick undulations back from her high forehead. By the time she was eighteen Elizabeth's black hair had had its first of many henna baths that kept it brilliantly red to the end of her days.

Now she smiled down from her superior height of almost fifteen years and welcomed her cousin. "Greetings to thee, Jane. Thou 'rt pink as a peach. Did the winds kiss thee or hast a lover, albeit thou 'rt but a baby?"

Her voice was deep for a girl's, and there was a kind of boyish good nature in her teasing question even while her glance shifted from Jane to the handsome cavalier directly behind her.

Innocently Jane smiled back and sudden laughter bubbled through her answer. "Aye, and greetings to thee, Cousin Bess. Well ye know the wind of the country is my only lover. It alone kissed me since I am come hence under the protection of so noble a Christian knight as the Lord Admiral. An' I'm

as ... ake him

... astime with a ...

... abeth's on the ...

... ulder at the Q...

... mething was ...

... looking up ...

... glance that passed between

the ... look of complete understand

... friendship, subtler than

... ng the great dog's head

... s, searching for reasons, or

answers ... ng to plague her.

... in the sixteenth century

... 's household, this has not

... except as it delighted her to

... turned to her father's ...

... ruary. This, too, had ...

... to stay near the

... Court morning ...

... ved at Bradgate

blowzy as a kitchen wench, the weather alone is to blame."

There was a silence broken only by the snapping of the fire and the noisy clearing of his throat by Lord Fitzwilliam. Of the entire company, Jane alone knew nothing of Thomas Seymour's unsavory reputation; that he should have been called "so noble a Christian knight" was striking everyone as highly amusing. It was true that she did not like him, but for this she blamed some unworthy instinct within herself. She laid her small hand beside Elizabeth's on the mastiff's head and turned to smile over her shoulder at the Queen. It was good, so good to be here; but something was wrong, something—and in that split moment of looking up and back Jane intercepted a lightning-quick glance that passed between the Queen and Lord Sudeley, a look of complete understanding, of something deeper than mere friendship, subtler than harmony. Standing quietly now, stroking the great dog's head, Jane let her mind race in circles, searching for reasons, for answers to questions that were beginning to plague her.

Being the child of a nobleman in the sixteenth century, going to Court as part of the Queen's household, this had not been extraordinary in any way except as it delighted her to be with so dear a friend. Being returned to her father's house after the death of the King in January, this, too, had been no surprise, though Jane would have loved to stay near the Queen during the long, formal period of Court mourning. Then out of the blue who should have arrived at Bradgate one morning but the dashing Baron of Sudeley, Thomas Seymour.

He had been closeted with Jane's parents for a long time and when finally they had emerged from the Marquis's study, all in the most glowing spirits, the Marchioness had called Jane to her. The bewildered girl scarcely understood her mother, so trembling, so choked with some emotion was her usually hard, cold voice.

"My child," she began, drawing Jane to her, "the Lord Admiral is taking you to Seymour Place in London where his mother, the gracious Lady Marjorie will greet you. Presently you will be again with our beloved Queen Dowager at Hanworth. Always remember, Jane, that you will from this day forward owe all your good fortune to the Lord Admiral. You will promise to remember?"

Dazedly Jane nodded. "Aye, Mother, Your Grace, I will remember." Owe my good fortune to Lord Sudeley? What good fortune? she thought. Why the Lord Admiral of all people whom I do not like?

As they jogged toward London, Jane riding pillion before Lord Sudeley on his mighty courser, she turned the matter over and over in her mind. Various things he said added to her bewilderment.

"My brother, Lord Somerset, and I are among the richly blest of the realm," he observed at one point, "he the Protector of our gracious King Edward, and I the guardian of so fair a lady as Your Grace."

"My guardian, you say, Lord Sudeley?" Jane tried to look up at him but her hooded cape was in her way. "What need have I for a guardian, my lord, other than my parents?"

The Lord Admiral brought his courser to a walk. "Well," his voice took on a fatherly note, "when a gracious Lady is in direct line to the throne, 'tis well if she have one other than her parents—one close to the Court itself—to act as her protector and guardian."

"Direct line to the throne? But my lord, I am in no direct line to the throne. Many are between me and it, and I but a child, Mrs. Ellen says, withal."

Sudeley's laugh rang out and his mount danced. " 'But a child,' eh?" A gloved hand patted her cheek and she stiffened. "Very well, so be it. But then is His Majesty's Grace also 'but a child.' Tell me, Your Grace, dost know His Majesty well?"

"Not well, no. We've danced together and once at Oatlands where the Queen had taken me for a short visit, we did play croquet with his friend, Barnaby Fitzpatrick, and His Majesty showed me his rabbits. Cousin Edward hath a merry heart but overmuch listening to sermons and disputations make him sour and lean of wit, so says my father."

Again Sudeley's infectious laughter pealed. "Ah, my brother Somerset hath strange ways with youth. Now were I Protector instead of Somerset, His Majesty would hear fewer sermons, follow more the inclinations of a lad of his years. By my faith, changes come to pass sometimes, eh, Lady Jane? Sometimes in the twinkling of an eye."

He seemed to be thinking aloud; and so they galloped along in rocking chair fashion toward Seymour Place. Jane's thoughts were still confused and uneasy when they drew up before the great door and she was presented to the frail little lady who was Thomas Seymour's mother.

Jane loved her on sight. Her gentleness, her wistful, big, dark eyes, everything about Lady Seymour bespoke fine breeding and a nature rich in warmth and beauty. Jane was embarrassed and surprised to find herself being deferred to, waited upon with undue concern. And when, after a few days of rest at Seymour Place, she was again on her way to Hanworth, the thought had taken firm root: she was being used for a purpose, but for what purpose? And why? The suspicion that was taking shape in her mind set her shivering as she and her guardian neared Hanworth; it turned her faintly sick now as she linked it with the glance exchanged between Katherine and Thomas Seymour.

The evening wore on; the Queen, Lord Sudeley, and the Fitzwilliamses settled down to whist; the Herberts, leaving for home at dawn, retired. Elizabeth and Jane on a hearth bench, their backs to the fire, played *cratch-cradle* with a length of silk cord for a while, chanting solemnly, "Crisscross, crisscross, sing to the baby Jesus," as with thumb and forefinger each found a new "cradle" for the holy Infant. The game was ancient, the "cradles" many and intricate, and the rules inflexible.

So an hour passed and part of another, while the girls laughed and chattered over their game. Then, "Her Grace, Queen Katherine, thinks well of one Master Miles Coverdale who is teaching me philosophy and penmanship," said Elizabeth. "I hear he will teach you, too, whilst you are here, albeit you have your governess, Mrs. Ashley, as I have mine. Did'st know they're sisters-in-law?"

Jane nodded. "Aye, my Mrs. Ashley is the very quiet one, they say, and . . . ."

"Mine hath a temper," the Princess interrupted, laughing. "La, and good use hath she for it, Jane. I'm no angel, forsooth."

"But why shall I have lessons with Master Coverdale? At home I have Master Aylmer and sometimes Master Roger Ascham. With Mrs. Ashley teaching me here, what need have I for Master Coverdale's great learning? He was chaplain to my royal grandmother, I remember, but—I do not understand. You are sister to the King with much need for special learning while I am but second cousin. . . ."

The whist party was breaking up and Jane's final words were lost in the laughter and chatter that followed. A cold joint, wine, treacle, and cake were brought in; midnight struck and presently Hanworth Castle was dark.

March blustered across the meadows to usher April in, then rose-garlanded May. At Hanworth life on the surface at least was peaceful. But as the days passed Jane's sense of insecurity increased. Something was wrong, just what she did not know, but that Sudeley was at the bottom of it she was certain. Why was he so often at Hanworth?

Elizabeth, Jane noticed, found him a delightful companion. The Princess and the Lord Admiral romped in the garden, playing breathless games of tag in and out of the myrtle maze, shouting, behaving more like six-year-olds than a royal Princess of fifteen and a nobleman in his early forties. The Queen—Jane marveled at this very conservative lady's attitude—laughed and applauded their antics. Jane, too, longed to join the fun, but something deep within her forbade it. Hadn't she been schooled in deportment for royal and noble maidens?

Then one evening in late May as they sat on the terrace overlooking the gardens, Katherine put down her gilt embroidery frame and smiled across at Sudeley.

"Methinks the girls should know now, Tom, since we've had the King's message at last. Say you not so?"

The Lord Admiral got up and crossed to her side and, standing behind her, put both hands on her shoulders. His bold, dark eyes sparkled, his lips parted in a boyish grin.

"Your Highness—Your Grace," he bowed ceremoniously first to Elizabeth, then to Jane, "I have the honor to make it known to you that the Queen and I are husband and wife. My brother Edward, the Protector, did not see fit to send his blessing, but His Majesty, the King, did most lovingly give his consent."

The effect upon Elizabeth was electric. Her cheeks flushed darkly and she rushed across the terrace to throw her arms about the Queen. "Oh, I'm so happy—so happy, Your Majesty!" she repeated over and over while tears streamed down her cheeks.

The Queen surprised at the outburst, quieted her, kissed her hot cheek. Of a truth, she thought, our Cousin Elizabeth hath a greater store of emotion locked up within her heart than we had thought, unless . . . . A cloud passed over her face and disappeared. But Jane, what does my little Jane think of the news?

Jane sat very still and straight on her marble bench. The pupils of her eyes had enlarged until the eyes themselves looked black; her face was ashen and her lower lip was caught between her teeth as if she were trying to hide its quivering. She knew she must say something and that at once. By a mighty effort she controlled her voice.

"Much–much joy to you both and God's blessing," she said. "An' Your Grace will pardon me now, I'll go to my room."

She managed a stiff little smile, curtsied and flew indoors, across the hall and up the broad stairs to her room. There she flung herself face down on her mammoth bed, and though no tears came, her body shook with sobs that threatened to tear her small frame apart.

The Queen, her idol, married to the Lord Admiral less than four months after the King's death! The Queen whom she had pictured as one day being married to some great monarch, statesman, scholar! The Queen who was all things noble, all things beautiful, married to Lord Sudeley! It *could* not be. What she just had heard was all part of some ill-begotten jest. Thus the girl who lived in a world of ideals and beautiful mirages built of her own loneliness, faced the ruin of one of her dearest dreams.

The months spent in Elizabeth's company had wakened

her rudely to truths she only had suspected. Nor had the knowledge endeared the Princess to her. What difference if the Admiral was *not* a godly or honorable man? She did not want to hear of his escapades. None of it concerned her. Or did it? Why was he on such very friendly terms with her parents? Always, from the moment she first had seen him laughing and strutting among the courtiers at Greenwich, she had disliked and distrusted the man; Elizabeth's nonchalant recitals of his gay disregard for every right-minded precept made her despise him. Yet the Queen had married him! It wasn't true! *It wasn't true!* It could not be!

Finally exhausted, Jane must have fallen asleep, for a voice softly speaking her name roused her. Cramped, stiff, she rolled over, sat up and dazedly adjusted her crumpled ruff.

"Y–y–y–es?" she answered, struggling back to reality. Night had fallen and the room was in darkness but for the glow of the rush fire purring in the grate.

Then the voice spoke again. "Jane, dear child," said the Queen, "I must speak to you. Come," she took a wax taper from the mantel, stooped at the fireplace and lighted a candle beside the bed, "I think we must have a little understanding."

Fully awake now, Jane slid from the bed, horrified. She, a member of the Queen Dowager's household, had been sitting in a sleepy fog while her mistress lit candles, a duty which she loved so to perform herself.

"Oh, Your Grace, forgive me!" She reached for the taper just as Katherine blew it out and moved the lighted candle closer.

"There is nought to forgive, dear. Come, sit here beside me." She sat down on the bed and patted the place beside her. Jane, on tiptoe, eased herself up and back. The Queen took her hand and held it while she looked down into the flushed, troubled little face. "Methinks, little Cousin, you hold no love for the Lord Admiral. Am I right?" She waited a moment and when no answer came she continued. "I speak thus because, though you are a child, certain things you should understand more clearly than you do.

"My Lord Sudeley, so gallant, so brave, has only England's interest at heart, as should we all. The hope of every loyal subject lies in His Most Gracious Majesty, King Edward. His marriage to the right maiden is of greatest importance—but all this I make no doubt you know."

"Yes, Your Grace." Jane's voice was a little shrill with nervousness.

"The Protector, the Lord Admiral's brother, Duke of Somerset, is a well-meaning man, but he lacks the imagination and the sound judgment of Lord Sudeley," the Queen continued. "Guided solely by him, the King might be led into any unwise alliance. Already he has said—I quote his words spoken before a group only recently— 'We shall marry only a foreign Princess, well stuffed and jeweled.' It was only his boyish way of saying he would marry any foreign Princess who had great wealth and an added fortune in jewels.

"The Lord Admiral feels—and most true Englishmen agree —that the safest marriage for His Majesty would be with an Englishwoman. Only so could England be strengthened from within. Because Lord Sudeley feels the House of Grey to be one of the oldest and most loyal in the realm, because the New Learning, the true Faith is its spiritual rock and foundation, he is giving all his thought to bringing about a union between the two great Houses of Tudor and Grey.

"If he is successful, you, dear, will wear the crown of England's Queen. Do you see now what a friend you have in the Lord Admiral? It took persuasion, you may be sure, to convince Lord Dorset that his little daughter should be placed under the guardianship of another, even so noble a gentleman as my Lord Sudeley. And it took courage for even one of such broad vision and love of country as my lord to assume the responsibility of such a guardianship. The Lord Admiral is your true friend, little Jane."

Katherine's voice was gentle as she spoke, her hand on Jane's warm and caressing. Yet, through a maze of wretched surprise Jane had felt the unspoken rebuke: Sudeley was trying to obtain the crown for her and his reward was her dislike. Was she not a little ashamed? "I think we must have a little understanding," the Queen Dowager had said. Understanding? What was there to understand? What, indeed, but that the person she most distrusted was doing his utmost to thrust upon her the thing she most feared, the Crown.

Chapter 6

COMING EVENTS

KATHERINE PARR had given her heart to Lord Seymour years before she married Henry VIII, but an inherent sense of duty, of obeying a royal command, added to natural feminine vanity, had made her the bride of the King. She had gone into the marriage with her eyes open; she had made the best of a grim bargain; she had been a faithful wife. Once free, however, she had turned to the one great love of her life: Thomas Seymour.

She was a bright and well-informed woman, this pretty widow, but to some things she was both strangely blind and deaf. Had no one told her how, shortly after the King's death, Seymour, bent on filling his own coffers and disappointed at not having been made Protector, had asked Anne of Cleves to marry him? When this stolid woman sent him packing like an impudent schoolboy, did no one mention to Katherine Parr that he had had the temerity to ask Mary Tudor to become Lady Seymour? After her blunt refusal did no one whisper so much as a word regarding Seymour's boldest folly, his proposal to the Princess Elizabeth? That she was a young girl, less than fifteen did not in the least deter him. But Elizabeth, while flattered by the attentions of an older man and one with the charms of Thomas Seymour, still had the good sense to write him that she considered all thoughts of marriage unseemly when her heart was so "sore tried by the death of my dear father."

Did no one ever suggest to Katherine that her former lover was suddenly so eager to marry her simply because the others would not, and because she was a very rich woman? Did she never suspect that as the dearly loved stepmother of little King Edward she was indeed a bride worth having, considering the rich political plums she was in a position to pick for anyone she loved? Did she really believe in Seymour's sincerity when he vowed friendship for the Marquis of Dorset? Was Katherine so blind as to believe this shallow, vain poseur was squandering his time on little Jane with only the good of England as his motive? Was she unable to see that if he did succeed in making the royal match he naturally would head an all-powerful party made up of the Greys, the Suffolks (since the Lady Frances was a Suffolk), and the Tudor family itself?

Was Katherine so immured in her romantic dreaming that she heard no rumor of Seymour's association with gangs of pirates who plundered vessels, then sold the pilfered treasure in the London market at fabulous profit? Were there no doubts whatever in her mind regarding the swaggering ne'er-do-well who was her husband? Apparently not—not at first.

Jane Grey, the ten-year-old girl had distrusted Seymour instinctively always. Not until now, however, did she realize how important, how deadly a part she was to play in his scheming. Sitting in her high bed, her hand in the Queen's, she learned the truth: if Seymour could bring it about, she would be Queen of England.

Her cheeks were scarlet and her eyes were suspiciously bright when she faced the Queen. "But Your Grace, I've no wish to be Queen," she whispered, whispered because her voice failed her. "To be Queen is to know much sorrow and I've no heart for it. Please, Your Grace, please, *please* tell my Lord Seymour that I do thank him for all his kindness but that I cannot ever be Queen. You will tell him?"

A strange expression flitted across Katherine's face as she looked into the girl's eyes. For an instant her hand moved, then lay still in her lap. Almost she had made the sign of the cross, a practice she herself had condemned ever since the Reformation, but had turned to instinctively as a wave of prescience and of great pity swept over her like a cold wind. She put her arm about Jane's shoulder and laid her cheek against the bright hair spilling from under its cap.

"I promise, dear, I will tell him," she said. "And remember, little Cousin, not a word of this to anyone."

The summer days moved in a pageant of color. Meadow and distant upland shook their banners of rose and vermilion and blue. The trumpets and drums of time marched forward and the fifelike notes of skylarks pierced the white September sky.

Jane was almost eleven now and just back from a month's visit at Bradgate. Somewhat to her dismay she found that Elizabeth, too, had returned to Hanworth, a little noisier, a little bolder than she had been even in July.

"Tell me, Coz," she invited the afternoon of Jane's arrival, "what did you to amuse yourself at Bradgate? Forsooth, 'tis a far and dismal spot, they say, with nothing but wild forest all about. What did you for entertainment?"

They were in Katherine's sitting room. Seymour studied a mariner's map spread out on the table before him. Katherine was reading. The two girls stood in a window ell watching an autumn storm lash the great beeches that lined the driveway.

Elizabeth's tone nettled Jane. Her color deepened and her eyes widened. "Bradgate is *not* dismal, Bess," she answered. "The forest is full of game, and truly the park is beautiful. As to how I entertained myself: well, Katharine and I rode our new ponies every day . . . baby Mary's still too young to ride . . . and, oh, the very best part of all was that Ned Seymour was there, is still. Ned's a big, strong boy and he had a golf club of his father's with him, and such strength he had that he could drive a golf ball far across the park, out of sight, really. Katey and I tried, but la, we tore up great patches of grass and the ball still fell only a short distance away. 'Twas fun, though. And Ned taught us to play skittles, too, and. . . ."

Elizabeth yawned. Skittles! Nursery chatter! "Enchanting,

I vow," she commented and sauntered across the room, and presently Jane heard her whistle to the mastiff in the hall below.

With a crackle of parchment a map slid to the floor as Thomas Seymour straightened up. "You say my nephew, young Ned, is at Bradgate?" Seymour's voice was low and Jane saw his heavy brows were drawn together in a level brush above his nose. "What does he there? Who brought him?"

Katherine lowered her head. Jane wondered why Ned's presence at Bradgate should be of any importance. "As you know, my Lord Admiral," she answered, "Ned's father, His Grace, your brother, is off to the war in Scotland. He hopes, so I heard him say to my father, to bring back the young Queen, Mary Stuart—for a visit, I make no doubt."

Even as she said it, Jane knew it was for no visit that the young Queen would be brought. Here was the bride for Edward! Here was a carefully made plan of Lord Somerset's being carried out with perfect timing while his brother, back in England, was planning the same thing with Lady Jane Grey playing the part of heroine. Jane found herself wanting to laugh partly from relief, partly because it seemed so amusing that two men, brothers, should vie so with each other and so secretively over obtaining a bride for the King. How grim a rivalry it was or what its cause naturally she did not suspect. If only Mary Stuart would consent to come quickly!

But the Queen was looking at her and she continued hesitantly, a little frightened.

"Lord Somerset brought Ned to be at Bradgate until the war is over and he returns," she said simply, wondering why Seymour should not have known it sooner, or, probing the thought deeper, why Ned should not have been left at home with his mother, sisters, and elder brother.

But the Lord Admiral seemed not to be listening. He was meeting his wife's eyes with a quizzical smile. He slid down in his chair like a schoolboy, his shoulders hunched, his arms spread out across the table.

"So," he muttered, "our brother will bring back a Queen, will he? And just to take no chances, should he fail, he leaves his boy child to act as cavalier and entertainer-plenipotentiary to the Lady Jane Grey and her sister. Hm, sweet brother!" He flung back his chair and stamped out of the room.

Jane looked helplessly at the Queen and her eyes filled. "What is wrong, Your Grace? I liked Ned and so did Katey. I—I—liked him very much."

Katherine held out her hand and Jane took the ottoman beside her chair. "Nothing is wrong, child," the Queen comforted, "nothing so far as you're concerned. But the Lord Admiral is aggrieved that his brother should be so bent on having the little Scottish Queen for our Edward, should think so little of England's good when he—but we've gone over this before. Let's speak no more of it. 'Twill right itself. I try to dwell on such matters no more than I can help."

Jane longed to ask Katherine whether she had kept her promise to speak to Seymour, but one did not question the Queen Dowager. So Jane would never know Thomas Sey-

mour's bluff answer when the message was given him by his wife. "So she 'hath no heart for it,' eh? Cunning puss! We'll leave her heart out of it, that I can promise, and so the steadier will her pretty head be for the crown."

Christmas came again and the New Year and Twelfth-night. Hanworth lay buried in snow, visitors came and went, fires roared up the vast chimneys and the air was redolent with the savory smell of roasting meats and browning pastries. Then Lent was tolled in from every cathedral bell tower and every village belfry, and breakfast in the great houses consisted of unbuttered bread, salt fish, and watered ale, with a concession of spiced barley water for the ladies.

Easter had come and gone and spring was in full leaf when the Hanworth household moved rather suddenly to Sudeley Castle, the Lord Admiral's estate in the Cotswolds. The journey by wagonlike coach had been of four days duration and as the unwieldy vehicle bumped and rattled its way over the hills, Jane thought of what had gone just before. That the Lord Admiral had quarreled with his brother, the Protector, she was certain. He had been glum and taciturn, had been absent from home oftener, and when at home had spent much of this time with Elizabeth. The Princess was a good tennis player, to the grave disapproval of Mrs. Ashley and the envy of her women. Day after day the tennis court rang with her boisterous laughter as, even in her constricting brocades, she beat the Baron of Sudeley—as he now was known—one set after another. She rode well, and together they traveled the forest bridle paths of Hanworth. And forever and foremost a romp, she challenged him to race her along the twisting garden paths.

Then one day after an especially hilarious romp, Elizabeth was no longer at Hanworth. Jane knew she never would forget that day.

Panting and disheveled, her frock ripped, her cheeks flaming, Elizabeth had run to lean on the sill of the open window of the morning room where Katherine sat sewing. "Oh, save me, Your Grace, save me!" the Princess shrieked hysterically, half laughing, half crying, looking back over her shoulder and going into fresh gales of laughter as Sudeley, convulsed with mirth himself, loomed on the path behind her.

For once the Queen did not share their mood. "Tom, have done with your clowning, let the child be! For shame, both of you! Bess, do you go to your room and make yourself neat!"

"Oh, come now, Kate," Sudeley, still chuckling, mopped his brow as he leaned in the window beside the Princess. " 'Twas not clowning, really. Bess hath the speed of a deer and 'tis a rich challenge to catch her up. Had I a son we would play so."

"Nevertheless, *I do not wish it!*" The Queen's eyes flashed. "One day mayhap you'll have your son, but meanwhile. . . ." Her voice dwindled and stopped.

Thomas muttered something and left the window. Elizabeth waited to catch her breath and smooth her hair, then she followed, and Jane to her discomfort, saw tears sliding down Katherine's pale cheeks.

The following morning Elizabeth and her suite left for the

royal castle of Cheshunt, and there followed a few weeks of comparative tranquility. Then the Lord Admiral was summoned to Whitehall Palace. From what Jane learned, he had been called before the Protector to answer some serious charges of trying to prejudice the young King against Somerset; of dictating a complaint to the Parliament which the boy King had written. The lad, when confronted by his Uncle Somerset, had broken down and confessed how kind "Uncle Sudeley" had been in his, "Uncle Somerset's" absence in Scotland, had given him extra pocket money, made him feel, well, ever so much more a King. And the writing of the complaint to the Parliament had not after all seemed anything so very important. Was it?

When Sudeley returned, somewhat silent and chastened, maids were set busy packing and a few days later they had set out for Sudeley Castle in Gloucester.

We're running away from something, Jane thought, watching the Queen's set expression. Deeper and deeper into the beautiful Cotswold Hills they rolled, passing remnants of ancient Roman fortifications, marveling at the snowy sheep grazing on the green hillsides, and turning at last into the gates leading to Sudeley Castle.

Jane loved the vast, buff-colored series of turreted wings which formed the main building. It was all so old, so very, very old, so shrouded in ivy through which casement windows peeped like inquiring eyes. Someone once had told Jane—Mr. Aylmer, probably—that Catherine of Aragon lived here during the time of her greatest unhappiness. It was, thought Jane as she walked through one of the many low arched doorways on the afternoon of her arrival, just the place one would love to come to for peace. Her own room, adjoining the Queen's, looked out on a little garden close. Leaning from the open casement on that first evening, drinking in the pungent smell of newly turned earth, hearing the sweet, wild note of a swallow, she felt a great surge of happiness. God seemed very near; she felt cared for, secure. The moment was brief, a lovely segment out of time, but she never forgot it.

There was much to remember of those months at Sudeley. Carpenters, drapers, silversmiths, needlewomen, skilled craftsmen in all the delicate arts of preparing a royal nursery were soon at work in the Queen's wing of the castle. In August Katherine's child would be born. Jane, whose fine needlework was the result of Mrs. Ellen's patient teaching, spent the happy hours of each morning sitting beside the Queen, sewing. And as they sewed they gaily planned for the baby.

One morning Jane held up the tiny cap of muslin and lace she was making. "His wee head will be snug inside it—like this," she laughed, fitting it over her closed fist. "And under his fat chin there'll be a satin bow to mock his dignity."

Katherine leaned back in her deep chair and smiled. "And cry you mercy," she said, "should he be a girl child, methinks his father would deny him! How my lord longs for a son!"

As though that thought bred another and one less pleasant, the Queen fell silent, and a May breeze lost in August's breathlessness, brought the stabbing memory of a petulant defense: "Had I a son I'd play just so!"

A few moments later Jane saw the Queen take a letter from the velvet pouch hanging from her belt and recognized the Tudor seal. It must be from Elizabeth!

Katherine was rereading the letter that had come the evening before, and certain passages in it brought a quiet smile to her lips: "I much rejoice at your health, with the well liking of the country, with my humble thanks that Your Grace wished me with you till I were weary of that country. Your Highness were like to be cumbered, if I should not depart till I were weary of being with you; although it were the worst soil in the world, your presence would make it pleasant . . . . Your humble daughter, Elizabeth."

The Queen refolded the letter and slipped it into her bag and closed her eyes to conceal the tears that welled suddenly in them. The child bore me no ill will for my anger, she thought, and I lashed out at her like any market wench.'Twas an ugly business. Has Tom forgotten? Poor Queen, she was destined never to know.

The long summer days moved slowly toward another autumn until at last August was nearly spent. On the thirtieth a daughter was born to Katherine. Two days later Jane tiptoed into the sickroom and stood looking at the red, wrinkled little mite lying in the crook of Katherine's arm. It looked, she thought, just as her own baby sister Mary had when she was less than a week old.

But the Queen—her beloved Queen Katherine. Jane felt as

though a giant hand were squeezing her heart. The Queen looked like an old, old woman, and the great dark eyes that stared back into hers held little of recognition. On the fifth of September Katherine, the Queen Dowager, was dead.

At first Jane refused to believe it. As a Princess of the Blood she led the funeral procession, a young gentlewoman bearing her train. But, walking through the winy September sunshine, kneeling in the ancient chapel where spatters of rose and blue and green lay in reflected beauty on the stone floor, even then Jane could not believe the truth. The *Te Deum* was intoned, alms for the poor were collected, and Katherine was borne to the crypt. It was not until hours later when, her heavy mourning costume laid aside, she curled up on her bed, looking out at the quiet stars, that Jane realized at last. Katherine was gone. She was alone.

Everyone was kind: gentle Master Coverdale; the nurse who had to refuse to let Jane take the new baby home with her; even Thomas Seymour, haggard, stunned to learn that some people were giving credence to poor Katherine's delirious accusations that he had poisoned her—even Seymour was thoughtful. Yet Jane was eager to be gone once her father's summons arrived. Sudeley, which was to have been such a happy retreat from all discord, had become a place of memories, of shadows lacking substance.

Chapter 7

A VISIT WITH COUSIN MARY

THOMAS SEYMOUR, Lord Sudeley, wondered by what strange alchemy a man's fortune could turn to ashes in his mouth and disaster come to perch on his shoulder like a chittering thing of evil.

Katherine whom he had loved after a fashion was dead and their child in the care of his sister-in-law, the Duchess of Somerset, whom he cordially disliked. His several highly dangerous enterprises were showing signs of becoming too hazardous for comfort. Once the Council began investigating he knew he would be doomed.

Furthermore, despite his boasts to Lord Dorset, nothing had come of his plans to marry Jane to the King. Sudeley was not a stupid man and he suspected his popularity with young Edward had waned, especially since the boy King had been persuaded by his Uncle Somerset what a rascal his Uncle Sudeley really was. Nevertheless, one could but try, even though it took more care and diplomacy than seemed possible for one man. To make the task more difficult, the Duke of Somerset had a beautiful young daughter of his own.

The war in Scotland with its unprecedented burning and pillaging had been to no avail. Little Mary Stuart had been sent to France to marry the Dauphin; King Edward was still without a bride and two pretty girls, Lady Jane Seymour and Lady Jane Grey, would have made choice difficult if the King had been interested—which he was not. Edward much preferred watching pageants with his friend Barnaby Fitzpatrick. All this talk of marrying was a great nuisance.

Finally Lord Sudeley bestirred himself and rode to Bradgate. Here he boasted anew to Lord Dorset that "If I get the King at liberty, I dare warrant you His Majesty will marry no other than Jane." For being permitted to renew his guardianship of her he paid Lord Dorset two thousand pounds, little enough, he thought, if he actually succeeded in his plan. But Thomas Seymour's luck, his seemingly infallible knack of getting what he wanted was wearing thin and time was running out.

Jane's reception when she reached Bradgate had been much as she had anticipated; with her studies laid out and waiting, and the Lady Frances torn between grief over the Queen's death and exasperation over the change which was bringing Jane home unexpectedly. In less than a month, however, her eldest daughter would face about and journey to Seymour Place.

It was October when Jane and her retinue arrived. The

Lady Frances, eager and encouraged by Sudeley's windy promises and his substantial reckoning to back them up, saw to it that her child traveled in a manner befitting the prospective bride of a king. Even Lord Sudeley drew in his breath sharply when he lifted her from the saddle, marked her heightened color, the softly molded contour of cheek and throat. By my faith, this is a lovely vixen! he thought apprais-ingly and wished the King might come cantering up to judge for himself. Here was a fitting Queen, gracious, lovely to look upon, and surrounded by an entourage so richly appointed that any Court on earth would swing wide its doors to give it welcome.

But Edward was not there, nor, as the days shortened, was there any talk of festivities at Whitehall where he was in residence and where Jane might have been presented formally to her royal cousin.

Jane was finding life at Seymour Place unspeakably dull. She read aloud to Lady Marjorie whom she loved; she embroidered; she walked in the park. And she wondered at the change that gradually was coming over her guardian. The noisy, infectious laughter was seldom heard; my Lord Sudeley's place at table was often vacant. And then on a bitter January evening there was a loud knocking at the great oak door. The Lord High Admiral was under arrest.

The specific charge was high treason and under it were neatly grouped all the major and minor crimes and misdemeanors that had colored Thomas Seymour's days. First came the charge of piracy on the high seas, then of debasing the national currency. There was grave though unfounded suspicion noised about that he actually *had* poisoned Katherine; it was known that he had bribed and influenced the young King against the Protector, hoping to gain the Protectorate himself; that he had brought undue pressure in trying to persuade the Princess Elizabeth to marry him.

All told, there were enough serious charges to have put Lord Sudeley in a modern prison for many years. But the sixteenth century did things more violently. After a trial which was a mockery, Thomas Seymour, Baron of Sudeley, was beheaded. The suddenness of the arrest and the speedy execution were appalling. Though she had feared and disliked him always, Jane shuddered at the savage brutality with which the bewildered man had been hustled to his death.

The calm, unfeeling comment of King Edward once he had signed the death warrant of the uncle who had shown him only kindness, made her wince. Said Edward before the Council: "We do perceive that there is great things which he objected and laid to my Lord Admiral, mine uncle, and they tend to treason; we perceive that you require but justice to be done; we think it reasonable, and we will that you proceed according to your request."

This from the wide-eyed boy with the strange, lynxlike duality in his nature. His tears had fallen on the death warrant as he signed it. Dear Uncle Sudeley, so generous with pocket money denied one by Uncle Somerset; so jolly, so ready with plans for merrymaking! Now that the fatal signature had been affixed, however, one's attitude, too, must have a clear-cut *finis* written after it: if Uncle Sudeley had been found guilty of wrong doing, then forsooth, it was quite right that he should die. One could not grieve forever, so one said, "we think it reasonable."

And the Lord Protector, Duke of Somerset, so grave, apparently so filled with Christian solicitude for his wayward younger brother, what of him? Had he, as Protector, stood beside the King when the royal signature was put to parchment? Probably not, for the unhappy man was heard to say repeatedly: "Had I but talked with my brother he would yet live in spite of everything; but those who desired his death kept me away."

There were others, however, men more ruthless than Thomas Seymour ever had been, who saw in the Seymours an insurmountable barrier between them and the King. Such a one was John Dudley, Earl of Warwick, Duke of Northumberland, a man without conscience and with an ambition that recognized no scruple. That ambition was to secure for his family by whatever means possible the succession to the throne of England.

Jane, returning again to Bradgate with her retinue, heard and saw little of what went on about her. Her thoughts were with the white-haired woman she had left at Seymour Place.

"My son is dead," Lady Marjorie had repeated over and over again, her eyes fixed on space, her hands folded resignedly in her lap. And at last Jane, unable longer to face that terrible grief without some human expression of sympathy, had fallen on her knees before the defenseless victim of an era's stupidity.

"Dear Lady Marjorie, Your Grace," she breathed, putting her arms about the sagging shoulders, laying her cheek against the white hair, "say not that your son is dead—please. He is not lost to you—he is but taken to his Father's house, as the Gospel sayeth."

The fragile little old lady clung to her as to a beloved grandchild, and when at last the day of departure came, she could not bring herself to say good-by. Instead, "God go with you, loved child," she said, her two small gnarled hands cupped around Jane's face. "One day we shall walk together again in the ways of peace. Mark you, it is given us who are very old to know these things. Until then. . . ." Her kiss on Jane's cheek was a benediction. Then she turned back into the house and through a green and pink glitter of tears the girl watched the lonely little figure disappear into the shadows.

Before Jane there lay two years of the most exhausting study. Roger Ascham, after an absence on the Continent, returned for a short visit. Then he was off again to the Court of Charles V and Jane was not to see her good friend again. Her studies were under the supervision of Master John Aylmer and a Doctor Harding, the rector of Bradgate.

One day to her surprise, Aylmer laid his hand quietly over the dulcimer sticks as she reached for them to play one of her newest pieces for him. Jane looked up, a questioning half smile parting her lips. "La, 'twas a trying piece to learn," she began, "but you'll see. . . ."

"Your Grace," Master Aylmer's voice was gentle as always, but grave, "I pray you'll not give overmuch thought to the making of music."

"Oh?" Puzzled, Jane tried to understand. "But I've worked so very hard—and Her Grace, the Queen Dowager encouraged me. Wherefore then must I suddenly give it little thought? Music is truly beautiful. Are we not told the angels in heaven do make music before the throne of God?"

Master Aylmer's mouth closed in a firm, thin line. "Aye, Lady Jane," he answered, "the angels in heaven be not mortal and the music they make is celestial. But mortals trifle with music for the sake of ostentation. I pray you put aside your instruments like a true child of God and a student of the New Learning. Be modest in all things, Your Grace, even as your cousin the Princess Elizabeth is a model of maidenly decorum."

Jane's cheeks flushed and she bit back the retort that sprang to her lips. Elizabeth! Decorum! Still, who was she to judge? If the New Learning had come to consider the playing of merry tunes sinful, then she must try to forget the endless hours she had spent perfecting herself on the virginal and lute and dulcimer. She must put her instruments aside. Why, she wondered wistfully, were so many of the pleasant things in life forbidden and wrong while all the uninteresting ones were unfailingly right? Thus did the ever mounting austerity of the Reformation touch one of its most faithful adherents. Jane had been a baby when the Reformation had swept England; she had known no other school of religious thought than that which had been inaugurated by the Reformists. To her the Church of England, the New Learning, was the Church. All else was something forbidden, unmentionable, something she never had known, and had no wish to know.

The following summer a plague of sweating sickness again settled over London and the two brothers of the Lady Frances, Henry and Charles Brandon, died. This left the Suffolk dukedom and the enormous wealth, the lands and castles it entailed, to the next-of-kin. Thus in October, 1551, the Marquis of Dorset was raised to the peerage, receiving the title of Duke of Suffolk, his wife becoming Frances, Duchess of Suffolk.

Fate had added to Jane's already rich supply of recommendations as a candidate for the title of Queen Consort. The great Reformers, Ascham, Conrad Bullinger, and Ab Ulmis, all agreed that in learning the Lady Jane had no woman rival in the realm; she was well trained in and a devout follower of the New Learning; her grace and beauty, her lovely, gentle nature, these were all common knowledge. To these now had been added the fabulous wealth of a dukedom. Such a one as wife of Edward, the King, would assure England a mighty step forward in the new march of progress. Thus the plotters, many of them godly men, helped the meshes of the web to fold softly about the unconscious girl; and the music was silenced and all girlish merriment banned

as a device of Satan—or of Rome, and to the Reformists they were identical.

But Ned Seymour had come again to Bradgate, this time with his sister, Jane, for another brief visit, a visit that had rendered Lady Jane Grey deaf and indifferent to the dreams and plans of all the preceptors and propagandists in the kingdom. She and Ned walked in the summer-sweet garden—the tall, fair lad and the tiny, hazel-eyed maid, and out of a silence that had grown over long, Ned spoke shyly.

"Jane, albeit we're too young our elders will say, I do love you. I would, an' you grant it, have you for my betrothed. What say you, Janie?"

In his eagerness he reached for her hand and the hilt of his light sword, more ornament than weapon, became entangled in the ruche at her wrist. There was the soft hiss of ripping lace and Ned's chagrined, "Oh, I'm so sorry!" Then Jane laid her fingers on the hilt while with the other hand she disentangled the torn flounce and smiled up at him.

" 'Tis nothing, dear Ned, and I'd—I'd—be betrothed to you gladly."

Just for an instant she stood so, her fingers feeling the cold metal and the torn beauty of the lace, and on her cheek Ned's quick boyish kiss. Then she turned and ran across the lawn, the terrace, and up to her room. *Now* what difference if one did or did not play a tune upon a dulcimer? *Now* what if Cousin Bess were held up to one as a model of all the virtues? What did anything matter? She was loved, wanted, not because of her learning or her relationship with the party in power, but for herself alone. "Janie" Ned had called her,— "Janie." They would wed and live in harmony forever. They would grow old together, their friends the great scholars of the world, their days filled with good works. Oh, God was good!

For a while and for the first time that she could recall, Jane thoroughly enjoyed Court festivities, and though she did spend a gala evening chatting with the King, all thought of the dreaded Crown receded like an evil odor that is carried away by a cleansing wind. She and her Cousin Edward would always be good friends, this Jane knew and the knowledge made her happy. The King was certain to give his blessing on her betrothal once it became formally established, which she hoped would be soon. But times were hard, and Ned's father, the Lord Protector, was hated by the peasantry he tried so sincerely to help by reforms, some good, others outrageously bad, and none of which they understood.

Northumberland, quick to take advantage, won the masses to him by promises and thinly veiled threats. Somerset and the members of his party retired to Hampton Court where the King, sick with a cold, was virtually a prisoner. Northumberland, with members of the Council, the Lord Mayor, the Alderman and the Lieutenant of the Tower, were at Ely Place, Holborn. Thus two armed camps were formed and presently as the number of Northumberland's followers grew, the Protector had the sick young King moved at night to Windsor Castle which was more heavily fortified than Hampton Court. The following day, after a meeting with members of Northumberland's leaders, the Lord Protector was arrested and sent to the Tower. The King, probably relieved to be free of his overzealous Uncle Somerset, returned to Hampton Court and promptly appointed Northumberland Lord Great Master of the Household and Lord High Admiral.

Those were the days when no man in high position could be sure of his life or the estimate of his honor from dawn to dawn. After a few months in the gloomy Tower, Somerset was offered his freedom provided he "confessed his guilt of presumption and incapacity" and paid a fine of two thousand pounds annually in land. Here was a staggering choice for a man who, no matter how great his blundering, had nevertheless been conscientious and sincere. He signed the "confession," paid the fine, and in a few months was again a free man and in good standing at Court—or so he thought.

Jane looked down at Mary whose puckish little face poked from her fur bonnet like the face of a gnome in a fairy tale. Quite suddenly the Duchess of Suffolk had decided to accept an invitation from the Princess Mary asking her and her three daughters to spend a week with her in the beautiful old Priory of Saint John of Jerusalem at Clerkenwell.

With times so very uncertain, the diplomatically-minded mother saw no reason for administering slights anywhere; and Mary Tudor, in spite of everything, might be the next occupant of the throne. The Duke went with his family as far as Tylsey, the estate of his young nephews, Thomas and John Grey. From there they continued their journey without him, riding in one of the vast wagonlike carriages of the day called chariots, escorted by a cavalcade of horsemen in the Suffolk livery.

Though the time was late November, no snow had fallen. But against the slate gray sky the skeleton arms of the trees waved their defiance to a bitter gale that lashed the land. Even the padded interior of the ducal chariot felt the icy wind.

Lady Mary wriggled deeper into her sables and grinned up at Jane. "Why must we go to Cousin Mary's?" she chortled in her rattling, unchildlike voice. "She is a Papist and a child of Satan. She . . . ."

Lady Katharine leaned across Jane. "Hush, moppet! Cousin Mary may, indeed, be a Papist, but one day she may be Queen, forsooth, and did she hear such words from you, whack! off would come your head."

Lady Mary continued giggling in sheer nervous glee, a terrible, old woman's cackle coming from a wizened child's throat, but before she could retort, Jane spoke soothingly. "Molly, hark, dear. Cousin Mary is a gentle and kind person. She is a Papist, yes, but one day she may turn to the New Learning. Who knows? We. . . ."

The Duchess whirled about. "Have done, all of you, with this chatter about Mary!" she commanded. "Whether or no she is a Papist, see to it that you each do your best. Mind you, no mention of either the New Learning or the Catholic Church. Let Cousin Mary lead the way in conversation, and do you but follow. Do you understand?"

To the back of her majestic neck three girlish voices answered, "Yes, Your Grace." But Jane did not really care. Her mind was on the members of the Somerset family. The Duke was in the Tower again, that much she knew. But where was Ned? What were they doing to him? His father, the Duke, had been released from the Tower and reinstated in some of his offices, true, but only a month ago he had been rearrested on—what was the charge? Jane wrinkled her brow, watching the dreary landscape slide by. Oh, yes, now she had it: he had been accused of plotting the murder of the Duke of Northumberland.

Surely he was innocent! And how could her own father have chosen as his close friend the terrible Northumberland? First it had been Thomas Seymour, the archplotter, the proved criminal. Now it was Northumberland. How could he! Ashamed of the disloyal contempt in her heart that turned her sick, Jane drew the fur robe more closely about her and closed her eyes.

Wasn't there some other way of life? There must be, she thought tiredly. She recalled the farm cottages she had seen so often when traveling from one estate to another, ruddy-cheeked farm lads tossing hay in the fields, pretty farm lasses laughing up at them through the powdery golden autumn sheen. What did they know of terror? They loved and wed and lived out their days in peace, serving God and their King. Did a leader rise among them, though, a dissenter whose views broke ever so slightly the even pattern of the law under which he lived and with what deadly swiftness was he destroyed!

"Jane, we're here!" The chariot had stopped, Mary was squirming out of her furs, torches flared. They had reached Clerkenwell.

Chapter 8

CONTRASTS

THROUGH the winter days and far into the spring Jane thought often of that perfect visit at Clerkenwell. Why should they all have dreaded it so? Possibly because Cousin Mary's reputation as a woman with a bitter tongue had frightened them? Possibly because they suspected a trap to snare them into defending their faith too loudly and so be guilty of unpardonable rudeness to their hostess?

They need have had no fear. Mary had come smiling into the great hall to greet them, arms outstretched in welcome like any good squire's wife. Remembering whose daughter she was and whose elder sister, the four guests dropped to one knee, but she raised them quickly. Sweeping along the little line they formed, Mary took the right hand of each cousin, beginning with the Lady Frances, raised her, and placed a kiss upon her cheek.

"Welcome, welcome all—especially you, wee Molly," and

she drew the crippled child to her in a gesture of pitying affection. "Come in to the fire. Jane, I wonder not that His Majesty's Grace, my father, called you 'a rare sweet child,' for truly, you are still that, an' looks can be counted for aught."

She had taken Jane's hand as they crossed the uneven stone rush-strewn floor of the hall; and looking at her in profile, the girl was struck by the unexpected sadness of her face. This was no cruel-hearted bigot; this was a lonely woman, frustrated from childhood by the knowledge that her own father held her illegitimate in order to smooth the way to his divorce from the mother she loved so much. That time had healed much of the bitterness between father and daughter did not remove the scars. In an upsurge of sincere affection and pity, Jane gave the large, bony hand holding hers a friendly squeeze. "Thank you, Cousin Mary," she answered. "You are very kind. I well remember His Majesty's kindness to me."

As they sat around the fire chatting, sipping mead and enjoying the honey cakes that were an invariable part of all pre-Yule gatherings, Jane studied Mary's face. It was long and rather pointed, but the forehead was broad and full, the eyes deeply set. Her voice, a rich contralto, reminded Jane of Elizabeth's. Cousin Mary was thirty-five, swarthy-skinned like her Spanish forebears, and her smile, seen rarely, was singularly warm and sweet. Jane found herself drawn to this strange cousin about whom she had heard so many fantastic tales. Ned would like her, too, she felt sure. Hadn't his father,

the Lord Protector and a loyal Reformist himself, been over-lenient, people said, in giving her the Priory of Saint John, knowing full well that it housed countless Catholic objects of worship?

But thinking of Ned brought the wave of unhappiness rolling toward her again. Somerset's new trial had been opened. If he should be condemned then his lands would be confiscated. What would become of Ned?

Jane started. Someone had spoken to her and she had not been listening. She turned helplessly from her mother's annoyed stare to see the Princess smiling at her from across the hearth. Mary had sensed the girl's confusion and repeated her question.

"Would you play something for us, Jane? I remember well what delight your lute brought to my father when you were of the Lady Katherine's household. I have instruments here—a page will fetch one to your liking, an' you'll play it. What do you say?"

Here was an unexpected challenge. True to her promise to Master Aylmer, Jane had not touched a musical instrument in many months. But she had longed to. There was, she knew, no ostentation in her love for making music; it was the music itself she loved. Frantically searching for an answer which would not be too antagonistic and still be honest, she finally came out with the only excuse she could find.

"I have not played in months, Cousin," she said. "Master Aylmer who teaches me most of the subjects I am studying is a strict master. He would have me perfect myself in those subjects first. Thus am I grown rusty, indeed, in my music. Not to do my best before you would shame me, so if Your Grace would excuse me, I should be most grateful."

It was rather a long speech and when it was finished Jane's cheeks were scarlet and her breath came unevenly. From her mother's expression, however, she knew she had done well. As for Mary Tudor, she smiled enigmatically and Jane wondered whether she had understood. Probably she had, for she accepted the excuse at once and without comment.

"Another time, then. I've some fair minstrels who can entertain us the while we rest before supper," she said. And when the four minstrels came—slender, beautiful boys wearing the green and silver livery of the Tudors—Jane wondered how the enchanting sounds they made could possibly have been deemed sinful by her Reformist friends.

With studied grace the boys grouped themselves well outside the wide circle of their audience around the fire. One played the viol, another the hautboy, a third a pair of light sparkling cymbals, and a fourth a small, tambourinelike drum. The little drum swung from the drummer's shoulder and was played with one heavily padded stick that lent a softly muffled, throbbing background against which the tune was played in beautiful, clear cadences. Jane's eyes shone as she listened and little Mary bounced happily in her chair until she caught her mother's eye and subsided. After the quartet had played several pieces, the Princess addressed the minstrel playing the drum.

"Come, Cyril, now let us have one of your songs. What of

the new song one Robert Weaver hath penned not so many moons gone? What is it called—'In Youth is Pleasure'?"

The youth bowed and, accompanied by his three friends, began singing one of the favorite songs of the year:

In a harbour green aslepe wheras I lay,
The byrdes sang swete in the middes of the day,
I dreamed fast of mirth:
In youth is pleasure, in youth is pleasure.

Methought I walked still to and fro,
And from her company I could not go—
But when I waked it was not so:
In youth is pleasure, in youth is pleasure.

Therefore my hart is surely pyght
Of her alone to have a sight
Which is my joy and hartes delight:
In youth is pleasure, in youth is pleasure.

Young Cyril was applauded and then, when supper was announced, the four minstrels piping merrily, led the company to the dining hall.

Grace was intoned, in English, by a venerable priest who, with two acolytes, arrived by a side door and then, the blessing bestowed, withdrew again. Jane was glad to note that the usual rules of etiquette were not so strictly observed at Clerkenwell as at Bradgate or Hampton Court. At Bradgate she and Katharine waited upon their mother, taking the dishes from a servant who brought them from the kitchen, returning the soiled ones. When their mother had finished, the two girls were served by their women in turn. Here at Clerkenwell they all sat down together and were served by men servants who brought the steaming food directly from the kitchen to the table, the contents of each dish tasted in the presence of the Princess before being placed before her.

The Lady Frances had every reason to be proud of her daughters' table manners. Not even little Mary licked her fingers after the roast goose, but waited for the basin of warm water. Nor was she less adept than her older sisters at tossing the bones politely under the table when she had finished. A less carefully reared child might have dropped them carelessly beside her chair to snare an unwary slipper. But not Molly.

The entire week was a success. At no time did Princess Mary intrude her religion upon her guests. Mass doubtless was said somewhere among all the vaulted, cryptlike apartments of the ancient Priory, but when or where the visitors never knew. A priest, Father Kirk he was called, intoned grace before meals and sometimes read aloud from the classics while the noon-day dinner was in progress. Then he withdrew and was not seen again until the next meal required his presence. Consideration for her guests seemed to be Mary Tudor's only thought; and when the visit was over and goodby's were said, Jane was wearing her Cousin Mary's Christmas gift, a delicate gold necklace set with pearls and rubies.

Her own gift to the Princess, a pair of champagne-colored gloves with the Tudor rose embroidered on the back of each, seemed somehow to be inadequate. But Mary smoothed them out with an appreciative smile on her lips. "They are beautiful, little Cousin," she said. "Thank you for your thought. Hast ever heard how among the knights of our good King Richard's day the gift of gloves betokened undying friendship?"

No, Jane had not heard. However, the idea was pleasant, and she clasped her hands happily in her great muff as the chariot rattled off over the frozen ruts, thinking how little she had understood her Cousin Mary. She was so kind, so thoughtful. And she had said in parting, "Come again—aye, come again."

The holidays lasted until well into January. As though too uneasy over some unspoken misery to settle down anywhere for longer than a day or two, the Duke of Suffolk kept his family traveling from one family castle to another. Jane met cousins of whom she had heard often but never had seen. She danced the romping *galliard* and the more sedate *pavane* and tried between gaieties to discover, if she could, the whereabouts of Katherine Parr's baby. What actually became of the poor little girl no one seemed to know . . . nor does today.

But at last the Duke turned homeward. Why should he dread so to return to Bradgate? It always had been his boast that in all the kingdom there was no estate to equal red-turreted Bradgate. Now he approached it reluctantly, or so it seemed to Jane shivering in the January cold. Thinking about it idly as they drove along, she watched a black speck approaching in the distance, a speck which gradually resolved itself into a man on horseback galloping toward them at breakneck speed.

When he came abreast of the chariot he brought his lathered horse to a buckling stop. The animal heaved and snorted in an agonizing effort to regain its breath, its nostrils scarlet, its sides black with sweat. The rush of icy air against the rider's face had left him panting, too, and it was a moment before, pulling his cap from his head, he was able to speak. Jane recognized him as one of the Bradgate hostlers.

"Your Grace," he panted, "I had word you might be coming this way . . . . We knew not but mayhap you'd want to turn off to London and we knew . . . ."

"Well, get on, lad, get on!" The plume on the Duke's black velvet hat, caught in the wind as he leaned out, stood straight up and Mary laughed aloud at the ridiculous picture he made, beard blowing wildly, feather waving like a flag of truce. Even under her nurse's hand clapped over her mouth, Mary continued to chuckle.

"This day, two hours gone," the hostler brought the words out in jerks, "the Duke of Somerset was beheaded on Tower Hill. All London's like to go daft with the shame of it."

"What! So soon!"

Jane heard her father's exclamation of astonishment and then the icy January world wrapped her in a blanket of oblivion.

Never robust, her nerves and health undermined by overwork across a period of years, emotional strain while at Hanworth and Sudeley Castle, and now stunned by the horror of the sudden execution of Ned's father, Jane suffered a nervous collapse.

Many weeks later when finally she emerged from the world of shadows into which she had withdrawn, Jane found she was thinking with a clarity that almost frightened her. Of one thing she was painfully certain: her father had known of Somerset's approaching execution. At Clerkenwell she had listened to speculation regarding the findings of "the twenty and seven noblemen" who had sat in judgment on the luckless Duke. Now she was certain that her father had been one of them and that he had dreaded returning to Bradgate lest the public feeling following Somerset's death should follow him there where he could not well escape it. Better far to be with a party at some distant castle where the impact of the fact itself would not be so stark. Well, Bradgate had been only a few miles away when he heard that the ugly judgment he and twenty-six others had meted out on the Duke had been consummated. That it all had been done under the direction of the terrible Northumberland she did not for a moment doubt.

What now, she wondered, of her parents' briefly renewed interest in Ned? Before his father's first arrest, when she and Ned had told them of their wish to be betrothed, they had smiled tolerantly as parents will upon any vagary of children. Then, after Somerset's acquittal and brief renewed popularity . . . there was even some talk of his being restored to the position of Lord Protector . . . the Lady Frances had spoken of having Ned come to Bradgate for another visit. Jane remembered standing by, helpless in the face of her mother's obvious scheming and hearing her urge her husband to join her in the invitation.

"Since the children are betrothed," she had prodded, "why not have the lad come for a fortnight and make the thing known formally? Just as well make it clear to Somerset who his friends are . . . ."

"Now that he's back in favor, you mean, Frances?" Suffolk had grinned at his wife like an evil satyr and Jane recalled her own feeling of shame.

But either the invitation was not sent, or Somerset chose to ignore it for the bait it was, because Ned did not come and gradually Jane had stopped hoping.

Propped among her pillows during the weeks of her convalescence, Jane tried at various times to bring Ned's name naturally into conversations she had with her mother. Her father came seldom near the sickroom. He was thinking of giving up Bradgate as a permanent home, using it simply for the hunting season and moving his family to Sheen, the abbot's buildings in the enormous Carthusian monastery on the Thames near London. He was remodeling much of it, landscaping it, making it a worthy rival of Sion House, Northumberland's estate directly across the river.

Of all this Jane knew nothing until one morning the Lady Frances fluttered into the room and sank into a chair beside the bed. "About Ned's coming to us for a visit," she began with a great show of casualness, "methinks for the time we'd best wait until we're settled at Sheen. We've said naught during your sickness lest the thought of a move disturb you, but we're leaving Bradgate."

"Leaving Bradgate? Oh, no, Your Grace, no, not leaving Bradgate! When I was younger with only the silly wits of a child I thought Bradgate ofttimes dull and gloomy, but now, after—after all the misery everywhere about, Bradgate hath the air of a sanctuary, a safe place that terror and heartache cannot find. Why must we go?" Jane was sitting bolt upright, resting upon her hands, her face the color of the white lace cap that framed it. She had wakened from a prolonged nightmare only to be thrust back into another, and desperation edged her voice.

The Duchess fingered her earrings nervously and assumed a more sprightly tone. "Come, child, here at Bradgate we are far from much of the jollity and pleasuring young people should have. Sheen is on the Thames, one of the finest restored monastic dwellings in the kingdom, and—" she broke off, laughing a little shrilly, " 'tis said it hath a ghost, just what you young people love. And across the river is the home of our good friends, the Northumberlands, with boys and girls your own age for company. There, mayhap Ned will . . ." she stopped, dismayed at what she had been about to say. How could Ned possibly come to them at Sheen, just across the river from Sion House? That fine property now owned by the Duke of Northumberland, had been the Somerset estate which the new Great Master of the Household had appropriated for his own once the Duke of Somerset was safely out of the way.

The Lady Frances cleared her throat. (Thank goodness, Jane knew none of these things!) " 'Twill be midsummer before we go," she went on, trying to cover her sudden embarrassment, "and meanwhile you will be making another visit to Cousin Mary, this time to Beaulieu. A change of air will bring back color to your cheeks. La, Jane, no maid with the air of a mouse, and a sick mouse to wit, can win a man, be she ever so learned and a Princess of the Blood into the bargain!"

She stood up, smiling at her own humor. "Have Mrs. Ellen get you up today. You've had enough potions and balms to give a well person the pox. A hard gallop over the fields would be my prescription, albeit I'm no doctor. And mark you, Jane," at the door she turned, "no more wailing over Bradgate. It is His Grace, your father's wish. Remember that."

In June Jane fared forth to Beaulieu on her visit to Princess Mary. Remembering the delightful days at Clerkenwell, she was eager to go and looked her prettiest. Her recovery had been complete and she had gained weight which was very becoming. Arrived at Beaulieu, however, she found she was not the only guest but one of a group of noblewomen invited, like herself, to enjoy the park and gardens made famous by Henry VIII. The King had fallen in love with the beautiful estate originally called Newhall Place, and had brought Anne Boleyn there at the height of their romance. The name, Newhall Place, had not appealed to him and he had changed it to Beaulieu—Beautiful Spot. Now it was Princess Mary's favorite residence.

The greatest religious controversy in the history of Christianity, the Reformation, changed many a friendly gathering into an armed camp. Catholics and Protestants alike were hypersensitive, fanatical in their zeal to prove the infallible justice of their cause. Hatred, suspicion, cunning, these were the order of the day, and the Man of Peace would have wept at the outrages committed by zealots on both sides in His name.

Jane came to Beaulieu, her boxes filled with handsome but severely plain apparel. The Princess Elizabeth, representing the Reform, recently had appeared at Court in so very plain a costume as to make the assemblage gasp. It had been a becoming costume, nonetheless, and ladies of the Court had been quick to adopt it. Now, to her chagrin, Jane found all the other young women at Beaulieu decked out in exquisite silks, laces, brocades, their delicate hands weighted with jewels, their flounces giving off elusive whiffs of rare perfumes. Their chatter, too, was gay and full of quick laughter and new, provocative words. Here, so far from London and the Northumberland informers, they were relaxed and having a thoroughly good time. And, Jane soon discovered, they were all ardent Catholics.

She was welcomed into the group most cordially, but the contrast between her own halting contributions to conversation . . . Jane knew no "small talk" . . . and their sparkling patter, made her ill at ease immediately. And did she imagine it or were there some suppressed smiles when she came into the hall at suppertime on her first evening wearing a gown that might have been suitable for a young novice? It was dark blue, relieved at the neck and wrists by a soft fold of white; and it had been copied from one of Elizabeth's most popular costumes.

At the end of her second day at Beaulieu Jane felt not only a rank outsider but an object of much ridicule as well. Why did I come? she thought miserably. Why cannot this visit be like the one at Clerkenwell when Cousin Mary and I seemed really cousins and not just two people who think not alike on anything? It was late in the afternoon and time to ring for her tirewoman. Supper would be at eight but before then there would be a game of *Gleke* which Lady Wharton was teaching her, so she must dress.

But before she could ring, there was a soft knock at the door and one of Princess Mary's ladies-in-waiting came tripping in. Over her arm she carried a magnificent gown of silver and gold tissue, and dangling from her wrist a dainty fan to match, all glittering brilliants and soft rainbow shadows.

"What say you to this, Your Grace?" she demanded, smiling as she held up the confection for Jane to see. "Her Highness sent it with her love and hopes you will like it."

Jane looked from the winking lights of the gown to the eyes of the woman who held it. The lights whispered an eloquent answer to her natural girl's love of beauty; the woman's eyes said, "Take care, take care what you do!"

As if answering that unspoken admonition, "What am I to do with it?" Jane asked miserably, seeing the reproachful faces of Aylmer, Ascham, Bullinger, and others watching her from across an abyss of Reform. She knew she sounded stupid, but how could you explain such things to one who did not understand?

"*Do* with it?" The woman fairly spat the words at her. "Why, wear it, Your Grace. Why not?"

Jane's mouth was dry, her lips refused to move, the muscles of her throat worked spasmodically as the needed words crowded up but faltered and stopped, unspoken. Finally, "Because the true Faith condemns such ostentation," she answered desperately, "and I am of the true Faith."

The woman tossed the gown on the bed. "Well, Her Highness will not think too well of such an ungracious answer to her generosity," she said, and flounced out of the room. Jane stumbled to the bed and threw herself down beside the glittering heap, too wretched to think beyond the moment. What else could I have said? she asked herself. How simpering the words sounded, how insincere! But I'll wear it, I'll wear it and show Cousin Mary I'm not blind to its beauty or unmindful of her kindness. But own it I will not—I cannot.

How much the Princess had heard Jane never knew. The shimmering gown on her tiny figure gave her a fairylike appearance and Mary smiled when her pretty cousin came floating into the hall and made her curtsy. Afterward Jane had the gown carefully hung in the great clothes chest in her room where she intended leaving it when she left Beaulieu. Perhaps, her guilty thoughts ran, Cousin Mary had not been told, and if not, then possibly she would think Jane had misunderstood and had believed the gown had only been lent to her.

But that was not quite right, either. A true Reformist would have made sure there were no misunderstandings.

What more was there to say, though? She was returning to Bradgate in the morning, leaving with her escort shortly after dawn. Several of the guests already had left; some would remain.

Throughout the evening, laughing, chatting, playing charades with the other girls, Jane furtively watched the Princess . . . who seemed just as furtively to be watching her. At last Mary rose which was the signal for the end of the evening's entertainment.

When Jane said her good night and good-by, Mary Tudor held her hand for an instant.

"Good-by, Cousin, and God speed you. And my greetings to your parents," she said. She did not add as she had at Clerkenwell, "Come again—aye, come again."

Chapter 9

GOOD-BY TO BRADGATE

At Bradgate, meanwhile, there were signs of upheaval. Carts stood before the door while men strained under the weight of mighty chests and beds of vast proportions and ancient suits of mail. Banners won in battle by Suffolks and Greys through the centuries were furled and carefully lifted into place beside jeweled swords and shields whose polished surfaces showed more than one deep gash. Magnificent tapestries depicting the Crusade of Richard *Coeur de Lion,* the crowning of Queen Berengaria, the Rout of the Saracens, these were given a cart of their own. And finally there came the treasures of every day: the cradles and baby chairs and toys; the *prie-dieu* from the nursery; the bowl of delicate rose glass in which Jane loved to keep green myrtle sprays. The family would travel by chariot.

Bradgate would stand deserted among its parks and forests. Deer would walk shyly across its lawns listening for the sound of hunting horn, the baying of dogs, or even the sound of human voices. But only silence would bear them company. Later on the Duke of Suffolk intended to use the estate as a hunting lodge, but it was a plan, one of many, he was destined not to carry out. It was as though Bradgate, deserted and hurt, chose to turn its back on the world and let the forests wrap it 'round.

While the Suffolks settled in their new home, just across the river at Sion House the Duke of Northumberland reluctantly admitted to himself that he was gravely worried. Thus far in his career every plan he had made, every scheme he had devised had been successful. The details of many of them did not bear close scrutiny and he quickly passed over them, for success always had been there at the end. Always. Now, by what devices of fate he could not imagine, his plans defeated him, melted into nothingness like ice before the sun.

He had ingratiated himself with the young King until the sick boy no longer knew which of his pronouncements were his own and which his new Great Master of the Household's. Almost too weak to think, Edward followed blindly where Northumberland led. This was all very well so far as it went, but, the Duke admitted, there were certain hazards. As long as King Edward lived and Northumberland kept his confidence, he had nothing to fear. By a little more scheming, greater monopolies, more princely estates like Sion House so easily could be his. But the King was dying. All the doctors who treated him agreed that a few months at the most were all that remained for the invalid at Greenwich.

Then what, Northumberland wondered, and shuddered. As long as he could remember he had disliked Mary Tudor. Back in the days when he was the Earl of Warwick, a young man in his twenties, and she a toddler tossed in her royal father's arms at Hampton Court, he had found something subtly irritating about the shouting, prancing baby. His fingers had itched to slap the tiny dimpled hand which on occasion had twined itself in his beard while Henry stood by, shouting with laughter, urging the child on to new mischief.

And through the years, as the little girl had become the harsh, waspish woman, his dislike had grown and he had done nothing to disguise his feeling. On more than one occasion, especially as his power grew, he had been openly rude, thwarting the Princess whenever possible. Now there seemed little doubt that she would be Queen, his sovereign, and that very soon. What would be her reaction to this man who, born a Catholic, had persecuted the Catholics with merciless vigor? How could he placate her? Where could he turn? What could he do to stem this ghastly onrush of disaster which was bound to overtake him unless he managed somehow to stop it? What about Henry Grey, the companion of so many of his forays? Henry, Duke of Suffolk, was a weakling, but he did have a fertile brain which occasionally concocted most interesting ideas. But first, what other avenue was open? Why take anyone else into his confidence? Surely he could think of something.

The Duke of Northumberland paced the terrace above the Thames, watching the swans sailing, like snowy men-of-war, downstream. Across the river the towers of Sheen rose out of the green woodland. Sheen—Henry, Duke of Suffolk—the Lady Frances— their children—what were their names? Mary, the little carrot-top, crippled into the bargain—bah! Northumberland spat into the river, his face twisted into a grimace of distaste. (He may not have realized it fully, but an idea, illusive as a sunfish, had slipped into and out of his consciousness, then back again . . . and he grasped it.) There was another girl, Katharine they called her, and then (the Duke halted in his tramping as the idea, shining and fascinating, came within reach), then, by the King's scepter, there was Jane!

Hmph! Funny, a month ago he had thought of a match between his youngest son, Guildford, to the Lady Margaret Clifford—like Jane a Princess of the Blood—but the whole plan had fallen through, just why, Northumberland was not certain. Had he taken the pains to discover why he would have learned that the Lady Margaret's mother shrewdly had discouraged every overture made by the Northumberlands. At the time the Duke had been furious . . . it had been one of his first plans to go awry . . . but now, suddenly and for the first time he was glad it had.

Suffolk would be far easier to manage than the Cliffords. Jane, hmph, somehow he'd always thought of her as 'that little Jane Grey, Dorset's girl.' Chuckling, the Duke brought his walking stick down with a thump. Ideas! Who said he was running out of ideas! First to Greenwich to make a masterly speech to the King, then a neighborly chat with his friend,

Suffolk. Ho, ho! Or possibly he'd better order his barge and go over and have that chat with Suffolk first.

Jane, and Katharine too, found Sheen with its cloistered walks and prim gardens oddly confining after the immense spaces at Bradgate. Everything was neat and trim; even the river wound sedately by, a shining ribbon to trim the summer's flounce. Across its unruffled surface the windows of Sion House sparkled and almost every day the beautiful barge from Sion came swinging across to the Sheen landing, bringing Northumberland callers.

The Duchess of Northumberland was a handsome, petulant woman who demanded constant attention from her sons and her son-in-law, young Sir Henry Sidney, who had married her daughter Mary. Even Mary, gentle, self-effacing, came in for her share of her mother's ill nature and Jane, watching, wondered how she endured it. There were games of croquet on the lawns that swept down to the river's edge, and putting contests on the velvety green beyond the herb garden. Card tables were sometimes set up in the shade and games of *Ombre* and *Mountsaint* filled the summer afternoons, with tall amber glasses of chilled custard to help one forget the summer heat.

One golden afternoon in late May, 1553, Jane looked up from her game to see two newcomers descending the terrace steps leading to the garden where she and her mother with the Duchess of Northumberland and Lady Mary Sidney played a final hand of *Ombre*. Jane felt her cheeks flame and her heart begin a wild plunging tattoo. Her mother already had risen to greet Ned Seymour and his sister Jane.

What did they talk about in the brief moments the brother and sister lingered there in the sun-splattered shade beside the river? Their mother, the Duchess of Somerset was still in the Tower; they were in mourning for their father. They were passing, they explained, on their way to visit relatives in a distant county and had stopped just to exchange greetings with the Suffolks.

The Duchess of Northumberland and Lady Mary, smiling fixedly, bowed and murmured greetings; Jane, her knuckles white as her fingers grasped the edge of the table, recalled the feel of cold metal through torn lace and willed Ned's eyes to meet hers. He was chatting easily with her mother, deferring now and then to his sister as she joined the conversation. He seemed very much older and Jane noted with a stabbing little shock of pity, how drawn and white his face was in contrast to the healthy ruddiness she remembered.

"Oh, look at me, dear Ned," she begged with her whole being, "look at me and know I've not forgotten!"

Instead, it was Lady Jane Seymour who turned and leaning across the table, put her hand over Jane's. "We do think of you often, Jane," she said, "and when we return and—and—all things have been made right, as I trow they will be, we must have a good visit. Shall we think well on't and let nothing balk us?"

Jane loved her gentle dignity, her complete lack of self-consciousness or rancor at finding herself suddenly face to face with the wife and daughter of the man who was responsible for their tragic misfortune.

"Aye," she returned the pressure of the other girl's fingers and smiled into the gray eyes, " 'twill be something to plan for. I'll love it. We can . . . ."

"Lady Jane," Ned's voice interrupted, "as my sister sayeth, we speak often of our friends at Bradgate and 'tis with regret that we can stop only for this moment now. As for future plans, time enow when—when better times befall, do you not agree?" His smile was impersonal, his tone friendly, but no trace of the old boyish eagerness or intimacy was in it.

"Lady Jane" he had called her—and he should have said "Janie." Jane kept her own voice steady when she answered. "Yes, I do agree," she said, and could have cried when he made a formal little bow as to any high-ranking lady, then bent over her mother's hand. In another moment he and his sister were walking across the lawn to the terrace and mounting the shallow steps. Jane alone had watched them walk away, so only Jane saw Ned stop, turn, and wave.

For an instant she hesitated, then, "Good-by, Ned, good-by, good-by," she whispered softly and lifted her hand. "Good-by, my dear, my dear."

The Duke of Suffolk and the Duke of Northumberland left Suffolk's study deep in conversation, their heads close, their arms entwined, their voices jovial. They had reached a perfect understanding. The next move was Northumberland's. After that they should have smooth sailing.

Crossing the terrace, they saw their wives and Lady Mary

Sidney moving slowly toward the landing platform where the Sion barge lay, its oarsmen drowsing in the late afternoon sunshine. Alone at the deserted card table, her back to the river, her eyes looking into space, sat Jane. As the two men approached she rose and made the customary curtsy of a daughter to her elders.

Her father noted the taut line of her mouth, the telltale shallowness of her breathing. "What ails thee, Jane?" he demanded. "Why such a peevish air?"

Jane looked from her father to Northumberland and back again to the scowling face peering into her own. "I'm not peevish, Your Grace," she answered, "but methinks the unusual heat of this May day and the bright spots on the cards have made me giddy. If, indeed, I did wear a peevish air that is why and not through any wish of mine."

Northumberland interposed a jocular note. "By my sword, Lady Jane," he chuckled, "if looking like a woodsprite alone here in the garden and not at all like mortal woman can be called wearing a peevish air as His Grace, your father sayeth, then may our wives and daughters all be sorely vexed and remain so!" The master of Sion House patted Jane's shoulder, bowed, ran a jeweled hand over his beard and looked to his friend Suffolk for support. After all, considering the project they just had agreed to launch, a little flattery to one so deeply involved in it could do no harm.

Suffolk's conscience, however, which had not troubled him so since Thomas Seymour's day, was again reminding him unpleasantly that he was wholly contemptible. The reminder

irritated him and he kicked at the sod savagely. "So be it." He ignored Northumberland's heavy chivalry and addressed Jane. "If thou 'rt sick go to thy chamber, else wear a merry air and join our guests." He snapped his fingers, pointed toward the three ladies who were nearing the landing stage, and with his arm again through Northumberland's, turned away.

Alone again, Jane began walking slowly back to the castle. Within the space of an hour she had had two bewildering shocks: Ned Seymour's changed manner and now the Duke of Northumberland's overt flattery. That Ned's injured pride, the disgrace involving his family, his grief and his changed position probably had much to do with his aloofness, this she could understand. But surely he must *know* that she understood. When would he come back? When would they meet again, renew their promises?

Northumberland's cordiality was even more disturbing. Never, since she first had seen him when he was still the Earl of Warwick and she a newcomer at Greenwich, had he given her more than a passing glance. She always had feared him as something evil and the recent growing friendliness existing between him and her father had filled her with a kind of horror. Why did it have to be? And now why this sudden show of fulsome admiration for her?

Threading her way around flower beds, hearing the cool drip of fountains, Jane tried to quiet her fears for herself and Ned and to be thankful for one thing: she need have no more fear of the Crown. How it had haunted her! But now, if poor Cousin Edward should die, and even Mrs. Ellen seemed to feel he could not live more than a few months longer, then Cousin Mary Tudor would be crowned Queen. Naturally, many questions about religion would be raised but they were sure to be settled somehow. Cousin Mary would be a great Queen who would be just as understanding and generous with her subjects as she had been with her guests—especially at Clerkenwell—and the country would live in peace. Then Ned would come back, his lands would be restored, and he would call her "Janie" again. . . . And so dreaming, Jane walked through the late spring twilight to the castle.

The Duke of Suffolk closed his book and pushed it far back on the table. His wife, playing *Solitaire* at her small work table nearby, laid down her cards and smiled at him questioningly. "Well, Henry, now that your mind is made up, what is the next step?" she asked.

"To tell her at once," he answered shortly. "The sooner the thing is done the better, and mark you, Frances, I'll take no nonsense from her. This, though she knows it not, is what all the years of effort have been for, thus I'll brook no argument. I would it were Katharine for she is made of tougher stuff and turns not a sickly hue if a plan is not to her liking. But," and he shrugged as he rounded the table and crossed the room, "Katharine hath spunk of the flesh but no strength of the spirit. And Jane is all spirit—which is needed now. Art coming?"

The Lady Frances laid down her deck of cards and rose.

Her naturally florid color was a shade deeper and she bit her lips nervously. The ordeal ahead would not be pleasant and she dreaded it, for indirectly she felt to blame. If, long ago she had discouraged Thomas Seymour and had pointed out to her husband that intrigue never paid, possibly the present situation would not exist. In her heart, though, she knew it was she who for years had been grooming her eldest daughter for just this result, though her plan had not included the present ugly craftiness.

Jane sat at the window looking out over the garden and river washed in moonlight. Mrs. Ellen had brushed and platted her hair and had rubbed her temples with lavender water. A cool muslin night dress had replaced the heavy brocade gown of the afternoon and over it she was wearing a robe of light China silk. Her head had stopped aching but she was finding it hard to relax. Her thoughts continued to focus on the two disquieting events of the afternoon and her whole body ached with nervous tension.

When a knock sounded at the door she paid little heed. Mrs. Ellen or one of her women would open it and doubtless admit a page bearing the evening dish of fruit and a pitcher of sugared water. But . . . she slipped from the window seat . . . there were voices. That was her father speaking. That was her mother's voice. Jane hurried forward, holding her robe about her, and the Lady Frances felt her throat tighten and her eyes blur for an instant. They had come to break unwelcome news to a woman, and this was only a little girl!

"Mother—Father—Your Grace, I—" she began, making small futile gestures to convey pleasure, surprise, welcome. Her father cut her short.

"I bring what should be welcome word to you, Jane," he began. He whipped a light chair about and straddled it, facing her across its back. "England has many fair noblewomen whose parents are hard pressed to find them suitable mates, men of like breeding, religion, worth. But among them we do not find the Lady Jane Grey." He allowed himself an appreciative chuckle and a slight toss of the head, and Jane, confused as she was, found herself watching the play of candle-light across his bald dome, and hated herself for it. "Your mother and I have chosen for you a husband who is in all things admirable: well born, heir to great wealth, and most important of all, a follower of the true Faith. I speak of Lord Guildford Dudley, youngest son of our good friends, the Duke and Duchess of Northumberland."

For an instant the full impact of what she just had heard did not reach Jane's consciousness and she stood staring at her father, unwinking, motionless. Then, with a great shuddering intake of breath, the girl's whole being seemed to erupt in a frenzy of words, broken sentences, entreaty.

"Guildford—Guildford Dudley—but I know him scarcely at all—Northumberland's son! Father, Your Grace, no, no, not Guildford Dudley! I'd far rather be dead than be of that household! I'll do anything, *anything,* Your Grace, but not that!" The words boiled up in a torrent as the full significance of the situation dawned upon her. She was like a creature at bay, looking piteously from one of her captors to the other, hoping for a sign .of compassion.

With a crash Suffolk threw his chair aside and with long, catlike steps, crossed the room to her side. "You will do as I say! Do you hear me?"

She stared at him in unbelieving terror, unable to answer. This was not her father who was often sharp, often unkind, true, but not a brutish ruffian.

"Answer me!"

Crazily words, names, began dancing before her and from them she selected two.

"Ned Seymour—" she began.

The stunning blow of her father's fist struck her head just above the temple and sent her stumbling backward. She would have fallen but for the high bedpost to which she clung, blind with pain and shock. As in a nightmare she heard the repeated command: "Answer me!" yet was unable to move her lips or to make a sound.

She did not hear her mother's frightened, "Have done, Henry! In God's name, have done!" nor did she feel the second blow when it crashed across her mouth.

Chapter 10

THE LADY JANE DUDLEY

AFTER a night of torrential rain, London sparkled in the late June sunshine. About the town mansion of the Duke of Suffolk in the Strand there was an air of bustle and excitement. Jewelers, hairdressers, drapers, came and went and already in the courtyard the crowd of alms seekers was gathering. The feast of small coins and food would be well worth waiting for because this day would not one but two brides go forth from Suffolk House. The Lady Katharine, thirteen, would become the bride of young Lord Henry Herbert, son of the Earl of Pembroke. Her sister, the Lady Jane Grey, would proceed to Durham House, there to wed the youngest of the Duke of Northumberland's sons, Lord Guildford Dudley.

Jane's wedding gown was a magnificent creation of cloth of silver and cloth of gold with wide angel sleeves, its bodice and girdle edged with glittering emeralds, thus to complete the Tudor silver-and-green picture. Her hair was intricately braided to form a coronet of braids and then was permitted to fall loose over her shoulders. On the coronet of braids rested an elaborate headdress of green velvet studded with emeralds, and wrapping the whole figure like a drifting cloud, was a mantle of softest silver tissue.

Mrs. Ellen had crooned softly as she bathed the delicate young body and anointed it with oil of rose. This was the baby girl she had loved since first she had held her in her arms almost sixteen years ago. This was the toddler who had come running to her to kiss the bumps, to comfort when draughty Bradgate brought sneezing and feverish misery. Now, four months before her sixteenth birthday, she was being arrayed for her bridal.

Mrs. Ellen's heart was heavy. A wedding was a time for much merriment, for roistering fun and dancing in the great hall, and the bride, like my Lady Katharine now, all blushes and fluttering happiness. But not so with my Lady Jane. She was making a brave show of smiling and of saying all the expected things. But Mrs. Ellen knew that behind the careful make-believe there lay a hurt past healing.

The faithful woman bending to fasten the thongs of the soft silver wedding slippers, found her eyes misting as she thought of the evening a fortnight earlier when she had heard terrifying sounds coming from Jane's room and then the Lady Frances calling, "Mrs. Ellen—Mrs. Ellen—come quickly! Her Ladyship has need of you! But hurry!"

She had gone running as fast as rheumatism and her heavy skirts permitted and had entered the room by one door as the Duke and Duchess were leaving it by another. Jane lay on the bed where her father must have lifted her, and for one hideous moment Mrs. Ellen thought she was dead. The delicately molded face was ashen white, the lips bruised and swollen, and above the right eye an angry swelling lifted the red-gold hair.

Cold water, balsam, poultices, these quickly reduced the swelling; crooning endearments, the tired body cradled against the motherly breast, these brought consciousness. But no healing tears came to restore peace of mind. Jane seemed to have passed beyond tears. Shock at the knowledge that she had been beaten into insensibility by her father left her numb. It was not unusual in that era for fathers, noblemen, and peasants alike, to strike their grown children. But to Jane, living in the world of dreams and lofty ideals she had built about her, the very thought of such a thing's touching her or any member of her family was beyond comprehension. And now she *had* been terribly beaten. Why? Too tired to think or to care, she lay, letting Mrs. Ellen care for her. So at last she had fallen asleep.

Tirewomen came to help with the dressing and as they stood back at last, looking at the exquisite little figure in its cloud of jeweled silver, more than one felt that here, indeed, stood a Queen.

Katharine, tilting her own white brocades in the doorway, drew in her breath sharply. "Jane, darling, thou 'rt like an angel straight from heaven!" She was lovely herself in the creamy white bridal gown, with her bridegroom's gift, a heavy pendant of pearls, glowing softly against her young bosom.

Jane turned and motioned her women to withdraw, then, as though floating on air, she moved quickly across the room and cupped Katharine's rosy face on her palms. "Katey, sweetling," she whispered, "thou 'rt like a beautiful rose, I swear. Now, promise to come to see me the very first moment Henry will spare thee, or better still, bring him, too. And Katey dear, one more thing." The older sister's voice dropped to a whisper. "Lose not thy faith—*not ever.* 'Tis a strange world and changing daily and only those who hold fast to their faith in God's eternal love for His children can survive. Be never afraid. God's spirit dwells within thy heart. Thou 'rt His beloved child and no harm can touch thee. Wilt remember?"

Katharine nodded and set all the jewels in her headdress winking. "Aye, I'll remember," she promised, then added with a relieved return from solemnity to joy, "And how glad I am, *how glad* that not a single bruise shows from thy wretched tumble a fortnight gone!"

Jane smiled and kissed her and pushed her gently toward the door. Best not to think of the "wretched tumble." She heard a slight commotion in the courtyard and looking from the window she saw that the litter which would carry her to the chapel of Durham House had arrived. At the same moment there was a knock at the door and her father entered.

The Duke was looking very handsome in his surcoat and doublet of plum-colored velvet and cape of shining satin, and something in his manner reminded Jane of a boy who is tricked out in his best that his courage to face an ordeal may not waver. Unwillingly she found herself pitying him.

He crossed the room to her side and took her hand in both his. His color was high and his voice when he spoke was unsteady. "My child," he said, "before you go it is meet I should tell you that all that has gone before this day has been done, however misconducted, with only your future high estate in mind. Try to understand that, will you? And believe me, one day, and that very soon, you will thank me. Come now, the litter is here and the rider has already gone to give the signal for the bells." With sudden unaccustomed tenderness he stooped and kissed the astonished girl lightly on the cheek, then drew her arm through his. Together they went down to the courtyard.

The litter on which the Lady Jane Grey rode to her wedding was at once a picturesque and an oddly awkward vehicle. A narrow, boxlike platform, its front and back curving gracefully outward in gilded ornamentation, held an enormous chair resembling a throne. Shafts extended forward and back and were fitted to two snow-white palfries, richly caparisoned and plumed, one in front of and one behind the platform. The bride entered and left her litter by a flight of delicate gilded steps held against its side by grooms of the household while two pages, one on each side, made sure their lady made no misstep. Had the bride been a Queen or Princess next in line, then only gentlemen of the peerage would have assisted; in the case of a noblewoman, however, even though she was a Princess of the Blood, household pages and grooms officiated.

Jane settled herself in her great chair. Above her, shielding her from the warm June sun, floated a canopy of cloth of gold borne by four pages who walked close beside the litter. At her right, mounted on his own big bay charger, rode the Duke of Suffolk, and around them in perfect formation, clattered a cavalcade of horsemen in the Suffolk livery.

As the procession moved slowly forward Jane tried with her whole being to realize that she, Jane Grey, was going to her bridal. Far off somewhere but coming nearer sounded the pealing of bells, wedding bells. Someone, some happy girl was being married, some. . . . She gave herself a determined little shake. This was nonsense! They were *her* wedding bells. In the beautiful chapel at Durham House her bridegroom would be waiting. Ned Seymour. . . . The sound of bells was deafening now, the litter had stopped. No, not Ned Seymour who was far away, who probably had not heard of the sudden betrothal and wedding.

Someone took her hand and a voice said, "Step down, my lady." Another voice coming from somewhere close by, commented, "By my faith, what a tiny thing she is, a mere child!" And another, "Them's the ones has it easy, eh? Albeit their heads do roll betimes, poor things!"

She must wait, holding tight to her father's arm, while the procession moved on into the chapel, the sixteen bridesmaids first, walking two-by-two, bearing bride cakes of pink sugar, and garlands of roses. Then two handsome pages came to cup their hands beneath her elbows, leading her forward, their wide sleeves decked with scented bride lace and rosemary, their every footfall, every movement affirming their awareness of the magnitude of their responsibility. Between them Jane walked forward toward the thunder of the organ and the splash of light and color which was the altar. Her eyes were bright, her cheeks faintly flushed, her mind and heart firmly closed over what she knew she must keep locked away forever. "Be never afraid," she had counseled Katey. From henceforth she would heed her own counsel.

Northumberland knew he must act quickly. His streak of good fortune was proving much narrower than he had imagined it to be. Jane and Guildford were not happily married. Guildford, his mother's spoiled baby, had quickly resented his bride's superior mind, her quiet dignity and fine judgment, and had turned bully. Jane, indignant, exasperated, nagged at, and spied upon by the Duchess of Northumberland, begged to be permitted to go home for a short visit, and was curtly refused. She was, declared the Duchess an "unfeeling, ungrateful, and ill-mannered girl." So, her bridal finery laid away, Jane found herself virtually a prisoner at Durham House.

An epidemic of influenza in a particularly virulent form was sweeping London and its victims were dying by the thousands. To the great consternation of the Northumberland household, Jane contracted the disease and for a time the doctors had little hope that she would recover. However, she rallied and was soon on the road to convalescence. Thoroughly frightened to think how close he had come to losing the prize he just had won for his family, Northumberland had her moved with every care, every luxury, to one of his country houses, Chelsea Manor. Then he hied himself to Greenwich for his carefully planned conference with the King. Every word must be perfectly timed, every inflection just right or the hypersensitive, disease-ridden boy might turn on him and his proposal.

He found the King in a highly nervous, irritable, almost tearful state. One of his physicians, determined to make the sick boy obey his orders, had told him how desperately ill he was—had, indeed, implied that he was dying. Not resentful but badly frightened, Edward had called for his Great Master of the Household who had a comforting way about him not unlike dear Uncle Sudeley's. Where was my Lord Northumberland? *Where was he?* Bring him! So it happened that the great schemer could not have arrived at a more auspicious time.

No artist ever blended his colors more painstakingly, no spider ever wove its web with more care than did the wily Duke weigh his words as he put before the King the grave importance of selecting the right heir to the throne when he should "come to die." Ah, doctors were great old grannies, he told Edward, sitting beside him, assuming an attitude of complete nonchalance. But one thing must not be lost sight of and this was an excellent time to attend to it, since the subject had been brought up anyway: life at best was uncertain and

England must never find itself without a King, an able, right-thinking King so far as his religion went.

Edward pricked up his ears, turned questioning eyes toward the Duke. A King. That meant a male heir . . . and where was there a male heir? By His Majesty, King Henry VIII's will, Mary would follow Edward and Elizabeth would come after Mary. But a male heir? Sister Mary was no longer young, and if she did marry it probably would be to a Papist. Beside that, the King's Grace had called her illegitimate for years. As for Elizabeth, well, Northumberland pointed out quietly, His Majesty never had been sure of her legitimacy either. It was only reasonable to believe that the throne of England should never be occupied by the son of a Queen whose background was shrouded in uncertainty.

But there was one . . . now came the great moment and the Duke found his hands were cold and wet, his temples throbbing . . . the lovely Jane Grey, only recently a bride, of the bluest blood in all England and certainly a leader in Reformed thought, the New Learning. Her sons would be the glory of English manhood. Let the King make Jane heir to the Crown when the time came and be assured that any son of hers would make a perfect King.

Edward brightened. Yes, Cousin Jane, a lovely creature. But where was she in line so far as his father's will was concerned? Fifth? Or even sixth? A pity, *what* a pity. But my Lord Northumberland was speaking again . . . one must listen carefully. By a legal "device" the Duke was explaining, the King could nominate whom he chose as his successor. Further, he urged him in all sincerity and with the religious future of the kingdom alone in mind, to nominate the Lady Jane.

Whether the sick young monarch attributed any part of Northumberland's vehemence to the fact that Jane was the wife of his son, history does not tell. Very sick and weak, fond of Jane who now was presented to him as the one logical heir to the throne, it is not hard to believe that he welcomed the idea enthusiastically. Then why not settle it once and for all? Pen and paper were all he needed. With the impatience of those who know instinctively their time is short, Edward demanded that the entire transaction be settled at once.

But there were stumbling blocks. Men like Archbishop Cranmer and others who were not blind to Northumberland's scheme, opposed the "device" as illegal and refused their signatures. Days passed with the King growing weaker and Northumberland more insistent. At last, worn out by the Duke's prodding, the dying boy is said to have raised himself up on his elbow and to have shouted with what strength he still had, that his commands *must* be obeyed and at once. The "device" was signed forthwith and Jane nominated King Edward's heir to the throne of England. Two days later, on July 6, 1553, Edward VI of England was dead.

Northumberland could scarcely believe his good fortune: Jane was married to Guildford; Edward had made her his sole heir; the Great Seal had (after difficulties, yes) been placed upon the document; now the King was beyond changing his mind and he, Northumberland, was the most powerful man in England. One obstacle still remained to be dealt with:

Mary Tudor. Until she was a prisoner in the Tower he could not feel entirely safe.

He took care that the King's death should not be proclaimed. Then a cleverly worded letter purported to be from Edward, was sent to the Princess Mary at Hunsdon where she was in residence, begging her to come to him with all speed as he believed he was dying and had much he must talk over with her. Deeply touched, Mary set out at once, little dreaming that a body of horsemen stationed on the road leading to Greenwich had been ordered to close in on her and take her, a prisoner, to the Tower.

But now Northumberland's luck received a blow which was to prove fatal. Sir Nicholas Throckmorton, an ardent Reformist but a man who hated Northumberland and had always been loyal to Mary Tudor, learned of the plot. He sent her goldsmith, a man whose word she was sure to believe and act upon, riding to head her off before she could reach the spot where her would-be captors waited. The goldsmith reached the onrushing party with less than a mile to spare, and after explaining his mission and breaking the news of the King's death, sent them galloping off at right angles toward a distant castle of Mary's where, surrounded by her retainers, she would be safe.

Mary Tudor would be safe. As for Jane—except as the lonely girl struggling back to health at Chelsea, represented priceless booty, was she of no personal interest to anyone in the entire length and breadth of England? Was there no knight in the whole realm to say, "Come away with me, lovely

lady, and have no fear for I'll take you far beyond the last boundary of this hate-ridden kingdom and you shall know love and peace and my life's devotion?" Was there no one? No one.

Rumors had reached Jane that King Edward could live but a few days longer and, so frail herself, her heart was torn for the boy who, surrounded by many, was still alone. She thought of the long ago evening when they had danced together as children and he had apologized for his awkwardness. He had been a pleasant boy, a strange boy, too, with his shallow eyes, his lightning change from humility to arrogance, so like his father's. He would die and another would take his place and the world would go on as though he never had been.

So musing, Jane had walked out into the garden at Chelsea for a breath of air. A pall of heat lay over the land and the late afternoon was suffocating. She started toward the river where an arbor facing the water offered seclusion and any arrant breeze that might pass that way. She had gone but a few feet when she stopped. Black clouds were boiling up over the river; the air had grown ominously silent except when a bird, whistling shrilly, plunged across the sky and disappeared. Slowly the daylight faded, changed to a woolly gray, to a sinister unearthly ocher. Fascinated, Jane stood in the lee of the house, watching the storm gather. She was not afraid but a feeling of prescience, of impending crisis, set the tips of her fingers tingling and her breath coming in long gusts. And suddenly she heard it—a far off humming, like a lunatic choir shrieking a hymn of liberation. Its horror held her spellbound for an instant, then a casement slammed, glass tinkled as it broke, and a servant came running.

"Oh, my lady, do come in," the woman shouted above the storm which now roared down upon them. "Mrs. Ellen sent me, her rheumatism not letting her go far. But 'tis a real tornado, this. Come in, come in!"

Standing at the window, far back and out of harm's reach, Jane watched the tornado which was destined to go down in history as the worst, one of very few, England ever has known. Trees were uprooted, beautiful churches and chapels were unroofed, farms were destroyed. And superstition added its grizzly tales. In one county a goodwife was said to have been delivered of a two-headed child; in another a nameless monster had been born. And shortly after midnight a messenger came bearing grave news: the King was dead.

A deluge of rain followed the wind. Lying wide-eyed in her great bed, listening to the rain, Jane tried to reconstruct what probably was happening at Greenwich. Edward, poor Cousin Edward, was at last freed of his suffering. Cousin Mary doubtless had been informed and was on her way to Greenwich. Possibly, though, there would be a proclamation immediately and she might even now, in spite of the storm, be riding to the Tower, Queen of England. With a prayer for Cousin Edward's soul and for Cousin Mary's reign, Jane fell asleep.

Sunshine and cool, fresh air woke her and she turned a smiling face to Mrs. Ellen the following morning. "I slept the whole night through," she announced triumphantly, then sobering, added quickly, "Is it true, Mrs. Ellen, or did I dream it—is Cousin Edward dead?"

"You did not dream it, Your Grace," the good woman answered, filling the bathtub from the big copper ewer, laying out fresh linen. "His Royal Highness is gone, indeed, and since an hour gone a visitor has been awaiting you."

"Awaiting me? Who is it, Mrs. Ellen?"

"The visitor is Lady Sidney, your sister-in-law. You cried out in your sleep often through the night so I would not have you disturbed. You needed your rest. Being young and impatient, Lady Sidney is well served if she must wait anon, for only so can she learn the virtue of longsuffering."

Mrs. Ellen sent bath water splashing furiously into the tub and lifted a beaming face to Jane. "Come, dearie, Your Grace. After the bath I'll deck you in a sweet new frock and put moonflowers in your hair and nowhere in the land will there be so fair a lady."

Jane's feeling of well-being persisted through her bath and while Mrs. Ellen, true to her word, brushed the red-gold hair and fastened a cluster of white daisies above her ear just outside the all-confining French veil. Poor dear Edward was at rest, so ran her thoughts; no need longer to wonder how he did during the heat. He was beyond the caprices of weather and of man. The thought filled her with a profound sense of peace, almost of joy, and she found it hard not to hum as she clasped the bracelets about her wrist and turned while Mrs. Ellen adjusted her skirts.

She made a charming picture a few moments later when

Lady Sidney was admitted and came rustling across the room, hands outstretched. Jane went to meet her and the two girls kissed. "Jane," Lady Sidney could scarcely wait to give her message, "I've been waiting well on to an hour and I knew not what to do, for they said I was to bring you with all speed . . . ."

"Sit down, Mary." Jane motioned her sister-in-law to a chair and took another beside her. "What dost mean? 'They said,' and 'bring you with all speed.' Where, Mary? And why?"

Mary sank to the edge of the chair but was too nervous to relax. "To Sion. Knew you not His Majesty died yester e'en?" Jane nodded and she rushed on. "Well, the Council, through my father, sent me to bring you to Sion House where they will meet with you this day."

"But what for?" The feeling of well-being was giving way to the breathlessness she had known in the storm the previous evening. Jane leaned forward and repeated her question. "Why would the Council meet with me of all people, Mary?"

Mary shook her head. "You know full well, Jane, that His Grace, my father, gives no reasons when he bids us do his will. Howbeit I suspect His Majesty, being fond of you, made you one of his heirs. More than that I know not. But come. The barge has been waiting overlong. Your things can be sent later . . . ."

"But I'm coming back—I love Chelsea." Like a zigzag flash of lightning, there cut through Jane's consciousness the memory of the morning she had heard they were leaving Bradgate. Must she forever leave the places in which she felt happiest?

"Well," Lady Sidney hesitated, "as you please. Only now please hurry."

Jane looked with sudden distaste at the breakfast tray on the table. She had wakened hungry for the first time in weeks. Now the sight of the silver beaker of milk, the buttered rolls and crisp broiled turbot upon its heated silver platter, turned her sick.

"But you must eat *something,* Your Grace," fretted Mrs. Ellen while maids laid out gloves and reticule and Lady Mary edged nervously toward the door.

"I'll have dinner at Sion House," Jane defended herself. "Instruct the women what to bring, Mrs. Ellen, then do you come with me." The possibility of leaving this faithful friend behind while she returned to hated Sion was unthinkable.

The ride down the river was pleasant or would have been if Jane had been able to shake off the pall of foreboding that settled more and more constrictingly about her as the hours passed. The morning visit from her sister-in-law whom she really liked, had not struck her as being especially significant. Mary had come to discuss family plans for formal mourning—nothing could be more natural. But the young matron's obvious nervousness, a new aloofness that raised a nameless barrier between them, began first to worry then to frighten Jane. A terror she had almost forgotten began pressing in on her and she fought it back with a defiance close to desperation. She would not think of it, not admit it within the circle of her consciousness. But it would not be shut out.

Sion House seemed deserted when the two girls reached it. A midsummer hush hung over the place. Serving women came and went quietly, arranging a bowl of flowers here, polishing a bit of brass there. Jane and Mary ate a solitary noon dinner in almost complete silence, for there was little beyond the King's death to talk about. Both girls, as by an unspoken pact, veered away from the subject.

Jane's moonflowers were drooping badly and she took them off as she stood at her bedroom window after dinner looking across the river where the turrets of Sheen punctuated the solid green of the forest like giant exclamation points. Sheen—what was going on there? What was her mother doing? And Mary? Katharine was not there, of course, but in her own home at Castle Baynard—Katharine, just thirteen. Perhaps soon now Katey would come to see her and together they . . . .

Jane's wandering thoughts were brought to an abrupt halt by the sound of hoofbeats, far off but coming swiftly closer, and before she could turn from the casement the first rider came into view. It was the Earl of Pembroke, Katharine's father-in-law, and following closely behind him came a "goodly companye" of noblemen, with the Duke of Northumberland bringing up last.

They made an impressive picture as they dismounted and entered the house. Jane heard the rumble of their voices below and had started forward, wondering whether she and Lady Mary would be expected to act as hostesses, when something on the river attracted her attention. The Suffolk barge was just leaving the landing at Sheen and was heading toward Sion House.

Chapter 11

A LEAF IN THE DUST

WHAT had happened? Was there to be a belated postnuptial celebration of some sort for Katharine, since the Earl of Pembroke was among the guests? But scarcely, with the Court and all England in mourning for the King. Besides, Katey would have been there. But in the secret recesses of Jane's keen mind the truth lurked, mocking her childish pretense of not understanding. She knew. But that knowledge was the terror from which she had been running so long and so stubbornly and even now she refused to acknowledge its existence.

Again the clatter of hoofs in the court as the Duchess of Northumberland and her suite arrived. In another few moments the barge from Sheen would put in at the landing; and while she stood, irresolute, trying not to give way to the nervous chill that was beginning to make her tremble, a knock sounded at the door. From the antechamber Mrs. Ellen came bustling to open it, and a page's voice spoke.

"His Grace, the Duke of Northumberland asks that the Lady Jane Dudley meet with him and the members of the Council in the great hall below."

The door closed. Mrs. Ellen, her eyes wide with questioning, crossed the antechamber and came into the room, her hands held out in wordless interrogation.

Jane flew to her, buried her face in the muslin ruffles of the old woman's ample apron, her arms about her neck. There were no words just at first, then, "My dearest child, Your Grace," Mrs. Ellen whispered against the shining hair, "methinks we both suspect what this ill-begotten summons means. There are times when, though we know not the reason for certain trials, we face them bravely, knowing they, too, will pass. Then is our reward measured by our grace to accept God's will. Come, hold up thy head. Let none see thy tears."

Moving with the practiced deftness of the nurse who knows her charge's every unspoken need, she brought lavender water, a fresh kerchief, brushed the straggling hair back into place. "Now hold thy head high and . . . God go with thee." She gave Jane a gentle push, then trotted before her to open the door and stood aside to let her pass.

Jane crossed the corridor and stood for a moment at the top of the stairs leading to the great hall below. The steps were broad and shallow and, beneath their crimson carpeting, rippled in a curving descent like an unfurled bolt of pleated ribbon. From the hall came the rumble of men's voices with an occasional feminine treble punctuating it; and by leaning across the balustrade, Jane could see the large group, all standing, facing the stairway, waiting . . . she was sure of it now . . . for her.

From the doorway behind her she knew Mrs. Ellen was watching. Resolutely she left the balustrade, walked to the middle of the head of the stairs and began slowly to descend. As in some fantastic, mechanically regulated dream, she saw the color pattern below her change from a richly hued mosaic to white as the company, suddenly aware of her approach, all looked up.

As she reached the last step, wondering what was expected of her, the entire company, with a clatter of spurs and scabbards and a rustle of silk, sank to one knee. Jane's gesture was instinctive. She held out both hands, palms up, with a quick little movement of the wrists which said more eloquently than the spoken word: "Oh, please do rise! I'm Jane Dudley, none other, and it is neither meet nor becoming that you should kneel to me."

She must have made an appealing picture, for a murmur of approbation ran through the crowd as noblemen and their ladies rose to their feet and made way for Northumberland who now stepped forward. Approaching the dazed girl still standing on the lowest step, he bowed, and then addressed her while he partially faced the assemblage:

"Most noble lady, most serene Princess," he began, "I am come to declare to you the death of our beloved Sovereign King Edward the Sixth. That he died in the faith of our Lord Jesus Christ and in the firm belief of the world to come we can only rejoice, for he was sorely tried and tempted in his last days. Yet did he constantly pray for the good of his kingdom that it might hold to the true Faith and be freed of the evil influence of his sisters. To this end were you, Princess, nominated His Majesty's heir to the throne, your sisters, the Lady Katharine and the Lady Mary to succeed you if you have no issue legitimately born."

Again the clatter of scabbards and spurs as members of the Council knelt to do homage to the uncrowned Queen and then, as by prearrangement, intoned together:

"Homage do we render thee because it pertaineth to thee, being of the right line. In all particulars will we observe that which we have promised, which is that by our souls we swear to shed our blood and give our lives to maintain the same."

Jane saw her mother, saw the Duchess of Northumberland, both looking highly pleased. Why didn't her mother come to her, help her find the right words to say? Why had she been permitted to face this tremendous crisis unprepared in any way except for the years of training in Court manners? Faintness brushed her lips and the tip of her nose with icy fingers. I must not faint, she thought. The thing I have feared all my life finally has come to me, but I am still the same person; I still feel exactly the same about everything. Mrs. Ellen said, "our reward will be measured by our grace to accept." Seconds are passing. I must say something. Dear God, give me the grace—let it be the right thing!

With consummate dignity she stepped down from the last tread and turned at right angles toward a massive table which stood between mullioned windows. Upon it lay a Bible.

Placing one hand upon it, she raised the other and faced the room. Members of the Council watched, fascinated, as the slip of a girl with the dignity of a Queen Dowager lifted her head, swept the room slowly with an all-encompassing gaze and spoke.

"My lords," Jane's voice was clear and strong, "that our most gracious Sovereign and beloved cousin, His Majesty King Edward did deign to nominate me heir to his throne, fills me with profound humility and grave misgiving. As ye know, never have I aspired to the Crown. I am untried in the ways of governing, inexperienced in the arts of diplomacy. Only that I am so nominated because His Majesty trusted me to defend the true Faith do I find the courage to accept. Albeit, if in truth it is my duty to succeed to the throne as His Majesty desired, then in all humility and putting my trust only in God, do I promise to govern the realm with all devotion and with what competence He gives me, and to His glory."

Having spoken, she felt suddenly drained of strength; her knees threatened to buckle; nausea in thick waves swept over her and she caught at the table behind her for support, head bowed. And slowly, as she gained control of herself, she was aware of an unaccustomed feeling of exhilaration spreading through every nerve and fiber of her being. Jane knew she was no longer afraid.

There was not much time for fear or for any other emotion in the heart of the newly proclaimed Queen that hot afternoon of July 10, 1553. She was hurried to Durham

House where she was given light refreshment and dressed in a heavy Court dress of green velvet shot with gold and having enormous, intricately wired sleeves. (Across the span of four hundred years the question persists: how could so frail a girl have survived such an ordeal, beginning as it did, before breakfast and ending, in velvet, not long before midnight on a suffocating July night?) History offers only the vaguest and most contradicting accounts of that long ago afternoon. That the Court costume somehow had been sent well in advance to Durham House, there can be little doubt; that Jane put it on and again stepped forth to go aboard Northumberland's magnificently bedecked barge in the late afternoon one is reasonably certain.

As the barge proceeded along the Thames toward the Tower, guns boomed their salvos. Northumberland had just had the death of the King proclaimed and with that proclamation another: the new Sovereign was the Lady Jane Dudley. Long live Queen Jane!

Just who was this Queen Jane? the common man of the street asked his neighbor. Why was not Mary Tudor, the King's older sister, Queen? A Papist, yes, but his next of kin, so the rightful heir. (The British mind is orderly.) The barge stopped at the Tower of London, that impressive group of Towers in one of which not long ago a newly proclaimed monarch must live for several days before proceeding to the castle of his (or her) choice. Thus the Sovereign became first of all a citizen of London.

As the barge proceeded up the river, Jane, though she spoke of it to no one, wondered why there was so little cheering. Now as she stepped ashore, seeing the massed ranks of citizens waiting for a view of her, she was once more impressed by the sullen silence of the crowd. What had she done that was wrong? Why didn't these people like her?

Had Jane but looked over her shoulder she would have realized that not she but the Duke of Northumberland, her sponsor, directly behind her, was the object of the people's detestation. She was not only the choice of his party but the wife of his son, so she must be despised. As she stepped ashore, teetering a little on the high clogs that had been fitted to her shoes to make her appear taller and so more impressive, women whispered together that here was a beautiful young creature, tall, graceful and fair as any Queen should be. Might she not do, after all, instead of Mary? But who was the stout lady of high rank carrying her train? Surely *not* her mother!

Walking beneath her canopy of cloth of gold, hearing the tinkling music of her minstrels like the nibbling of mice against the thunderous booming of the cannons' salute, Jane longed to scream her humiliation. Behind her, all but stumbling under the weight of the tremendous train she insisted on carrying alone, the Duchess of Suffolk staggered along behind her daughter. Before Jane, stepping backwards, bowing low at intervals, her father made himself (and her) ridiculous as her most abjectly humble subject. Thus was shame added to the burden of misery she carried with her into the Tower. A writer of the day called it "a most despicable and humiliating sight."

Once she had entered the Tower, Heralds trumpeted and "the Quene's proclamation" was read at the four corners of London. It was a bumptious, shockingly worded document in which both the Princess Mary and the Princess Elizabeth were referred to repeatedly in most offensive terms. It aroused the hatred of Catholics and Protestants alike who recognized it as a masterwork of Northumberland's. They cared little for the new "Quene" about whom they had heard nothing until the moment of her succession to the throne. However, that she was a tool of the despised Northumberland's they never doubted and for that they hated her.

Jane's first day as Queen drew to a close and, completely exhausted, she fell asleep in the great bed where so many queens before her had slept. What, she wondered, had beautiful little Anne Boleyn thought as she dozed off, little dreaming that in the neighboring White Tower she would pay with her life for her indiscretions when life at Court had become tasteless and dull? What had. . . ? And then Queen Jane was asleep.

Dawn, like a straggler returning from a night's revelry, crept into the Tower. There was no hint of sunshine; clouds, gray and rain-clogged, hung over the city. Within the Tower enclosure scullery maids moved sleepily about their first tasks; warders changed their posts; from the river came the first cries and hellos of bargemen. In her bed the young Queen opened her eyes and looked about her.

Had it been only yesterday morning that she left Chelsea? This, then, was her second day as Queen. Queen! Jane folded her arms behind her head and lay staring into the murky half-light. Yesterday's comparative success had given her confidence. She had managed that, so perhaps she could manage other situations that troubled her as well. I will be a good Queen, she thought. I will heed the advice of the Council when I feel it is right and debate calmly with them when I am not sure. There shall be an end once and forever to burnings and torture, no matter how grave the felony. I will by example show that the true Faith is founded on brotherly love and mercy, not terror. Perhaps, who knows, this thing I have feared so long may prove a blessing to England after all.

She must have dozed, for Mrs. Ellen's voice roused her. Her bath was ready, her mistress of the wardrobe waiting to consult her on today's apparel. The Lord High Treasurer, the Marquis of Winchester, was coming to fit the crown. The Council would meet before noon. Yes, yes, of course. These matters were important, too. One could not lie abed dreaming of the great deeds one would do; one must be up and doing.

Jane was still at her dressing table when, following a peremptory knock, Guildford Dudley and his mother strode into the room. A wave of anger surged through the Queen. How dared they violate one's privacy so! Whether she was simply Jane Dudley or the Queen of England, how dared anyone intrude thus without so much as an apology! With bitter amusement she thought of yesterday's kneeling and bowing and fawning from this same ill-mannered woman, and was hard put to it not to burst out laughing.

"Yes?" She turned from the mirror and faced her husband and mother-in-law. "Good morrow, Guildford, and to Your Grace, good morrow."

Guildford, his face crimson, stammered something incoherent. The Duchess, however, wasted no time. "A fine business this," she shouted, "a very fine business, indeed! First my Lady Jane, having taken my son as husband, runs away to Chelsea on the pretext . . . ah, yes, I know, I know, my husband encouraged it . . . that she must have rest and country air and must be alone to commune with whatever daft powers she gleans from all her reading in books not intended for womankind. That is not enough. . . ."

"Madam, please!"

". . . not enough. She must wrest the crown from her husband who rightly should wear it. Queen! Bah! Queen Consort, mayhap, but not Queen, my young miss, not Queen! England must have a King! So it was intended." The Duchess was breathing in mighty gusts, her face was purple. "I came hither this morning, bringing Guildford, to inquire just when you will deign to let him return to you as your husband, for your husband he is. In the chamber without, whom should I meet but the Marquis of Winchester. What has he to say? That he 'awaits Her Majesty's pleasure to try on the crown.' "

"Ah, then he is come," Jane interrupted, glad for an

opening. But her mother-in-law rushed on. " 'Well,' said I, 'and here is the King to be measured for *his* crown,' and Winchester . . . oh, he shall pay for this! . . . answered, 'As to that, Her Majesty will decide.' 'Her Majesty' indeed! What hast to say, Jane?"

Anger at the woman's stupid effrontery held her silent for a moment, then, "Your Grace, let us not speak in bitterness," she answered quietly. "Whether we like it or no, *I am the Queen*. . . . Just a moment," as the Duchess attempted to resume. "I was so nominated by our beloved cousin, King Edward, and so proclaimed by the Council. Parliament today will ratify it. It is meet and right that I make Guildford a Duke, which I shall most happily, but only by an act of Parliament can he be made King. Neither I nor any other living being has that right. If my word is not enough, Madam, there is always the Council."

For a moment the Duchess hesitated. Fury had stemmed if it had not entirely stopped her tirade. She held out her hand to Guildford. "Come, my son. This woman is no Queen, but a vixen and a jade," she said. "Come back to Sion with me and we shall see how the people like a Queen who cannot live at peace with her own husband."

She flounced out of the room, dragging Guildford after her. At the threshold the boy turned and looked back, ashamed that his eyes were brimming and his heart heavy.

Jane sank down on her dressing chair, looking at her tightly clasped hands. Had she "managed" this time? Or should she have had the shouting termagant put out of the room? And Guildford, poor Guildford, so much the boy, so little the man, so unsure of himself. Did he, poor lad, think the Crown, the Crown she did not want but was bound to wear, was a child's toy to be given by her at will to anyone of her choice? How much misinformation had his mother given him?

"Janie?"

Jane started as though she had been struck. Ned's name for her—Janie. A firm, boyish hand came down quietly on the dressing table to rest there among the jeweled boxes and bottles, and her eyes, following it up the handsome velvet sleeve, came at last to Guildford's flushed young face. Guildford, her husband.

"Janie, be not angry with me," he pleaded, sinking to his knees the better to look into her eyes. "The Earls of Pembroke and Arundel were waiting without when my mother and I did come from your chamber and they urged me . . . not that I needed urging . . . to return to you. Her Grace bade me in great anger to go to Sion, but—but I did not go. Jane—Your Majesty—my wife"—the boy's voice fell to a whisper—"may I stay?"

Jane laid her hand over his among the paraphernalia on the table. "Yes, Guildford, my husband," she answered quietly, "you may stay an' you care to." He tilted her chin up for his kiss, then his arms went around her.

The days following were filled for the young Queen with new and exacting duties. She must accustom herself to meeting with her Council; she must hear long and tiresome speeches and understand and remember them; she must sit for her portrait; she must inspect and officially accept the crown jewels; she must select from the countless bolts brought to her the exact shade of purple she wanted for her coronation robes. The summer heat continued, her gowns were heavy, the high clogs on which she walked tired her and left her back and legs aching cruelly. But, having accepted her lot, she was determined to carry on as she felt a Queen should —without complaint.

Meanwhile in Norfolk Princess Mary was savoring that rare thing: unqualified loyalty. In the country lanes, from the highways and byways, from the small farms and landed estates came supporters of King Henry's daughter, King Edward's half sister. They'd have none of the Northumberlands. Away with them, with their whole breed! Long live Queen Mary!

Like wildfire the indignation ran, igniting every county, every town, every hamlet, until all England seemed aflame with one desire: to rid itself of Queen Jane and place Mary safely on the throne. Thirty thousand men were said to be marching on London.

Stunned, Northumberland gathered an army about him, a pitifully small army in comparison to the one he would meet. As an added strategic move which he believed would practically guarantee the capture of Mary should she attempt an escape by sea, he had ordered six men-of-war to cruise along the coast. To capture her and bring her back, a prisoner, should be simple.

But suddenly nothing was simple. With the passing of the days, Jane saw her Council desert her. Pembroke, Winchester, Arundel, the very men who, little more than a week ago, had sworn to die for her and her cause if need be, got themselves quietly out of the Tower. As swiftly as horses could carry them there, they gathered at Castle Baynard where Pembroke made a fiery speech denouncing Northumberland and the young Queen he had so cold-bloodedly maneuvered to the throne. Then to Cheapside where, with heralds going before them, they proclaimed Mary Tudor Queen of England.

Sitting alone and forlorn in her huge gilded chair in the Council Chamber, Jane realized matters were going awry. Otherwise, why had the Council, once she had dismissed it, rushed away so, with such purpose? Was it possible that after all, Cousin Mary could want the throne, just as the letter read before the Council by the Duke of Northumberland had implied? And if it were true, then, well . . . ?

Hope surged up within her. In no wise would she betray the trust that had been left in her hands by her dying cousin, but if Cousin Mary *did* want the hated Crown. . . and somehow, in spite of everything, she did seem the rightful heir. . . surely a way could be found to give it to her without jeopardizing the true Faith. If only Mary would come soon that they might talk it over!

Torn between hope of release from her unwelcome Queenship and fear that such a release would plunge her into a sea of self-accusation for the rest of her life, she sat huddled beneath the gold canopy of State, wondering what to do, what was expected of her in the present crisis. She was to have been godmother that afternoon to the baby of a young minister working within the Tower, but had found herself too tired to attend the ceremony and had sent Lady Throckmorton, a member of her suite, to take her place, acting as proxy. Now, with time on her hands, Jane welcomed the thought of lying down for an afternoon of rest.

She just had risen to her feet to step from the dais when there came the shattering roar of a cannon nearby and with it the sound of shouting. What did the voices cry? And as she stood, trying to catch the words, she saw her father enter the Council Chamber and begin walking up its cluttered length, past the chairs left overturned, past the great table with its litter of torn parchments, to stand beside her. He looked old and sick and haggard, his eyes bloodshot.

Jane ran to meet him. "What is it, Father?" she began. "Are the soldiers returning? Think you I should greet them?"

Suffolk looked at the frail child he had forced into the hideous predicament she now faced and his very being sickened. "No, my child," he answered and took her hand. "Come down from there. The dream is ended. I should have known. You are no longer Queen. Listen!"

Closer, clearer came the triumphant shouting: "Long live Queen Mary! Hail Queen Mary!" The nine-day reign of Queen Jane was over.

Color rushed into Jane's white cheeks. "Now may I go home?" she asked breathlessly. Only when her father continued to shake his head and for the first time in her memory held out his arms to her did she realize the truth. She was a prisoner.

Summer passed and autumn faded the roses in the Tower garden. Jane lived with Mrs. Ellen and several of her favorite women in a simple cottage in the enclosure. That she eventually would be free she was certain. Cousin Mary, once she understood all the circumstances, would send for her and they would talk together as they had at Clerkenwell so long ago. Then she would go home to Sheen—no, there was Guildford. Possibly they could go to a home of their own somewhere far from Sion House—someday there might be children. . . . Thus she dreamed beside the window during the first days of autumn.

Guildford was held in one of the prison towers and she saw him seldom. She had become fond of the petulant, high-strung boy who seemed to love her so, and she had learned to close her mind to the fact that his father was the terrible Northumberland and his mother the screaming shrew she was.

Northumberland was executed late in August. Jane had disliked him with her whole heart, but the past few months had brought him within the inner circle of her acquaintances and his death shocked her in a way she did not understand.

On November 13, a day of blue skies and winy sunshine, Jane and Guildford were summoned to appear at Guildhall for trial. The accusation brought against them was high treason, and Mary had sat long over the wording of it. Little

Jane . . . no, that child had no thought of treason in her lovely head. Still, ...

The verdict was guilty.

Now Christmas must pass, a bleak time when far-off bells rang out the midnight tale of Peace on Earth and families gathered in happiness about their firesides. January came in with stinging sleet, and Mary, the Queen, sitting before her writing table, looked over a sheaf of papers a secretary just had handed her. They were death warrants. At one she stopped and bit her lip and her color changed. The warrant before her bore the name of Jane Dudley. For a moment she hesitated, looking out into the storm, seeing—what? Clerkenwell? Beaulieu? Her own wretched girlhood? Then, with a strange little sound, half sob, half exclamation of impatience, she dipped her quill in the ink, signed the warrant and sanded it.

Now it was February and just the faintest hint of spring showed here and there in the path borders and the ivy clinging to walls and pasture stiles. Jane wished her women would not weep so. Over and over again she had tried to explain to them that death would be release; that life had been prolonged heartache and loneliness. Nor was she afraid. Fear had slipped from her like an ill-fitting garment—when was it?—when she had acknowledged her sovereignty in the great hall at Sion. Now, though at times the pounding of her heart threatened to suffocate her and her hands grew cold and wet as waves of nervousness crept over her, actual terror withdrew and outwardly she was calm.

The evening of Sunday, February 11, 1554, passed quietly. Jane sat with Mrs. Ellen, her head against the comfortable shoulder where so often it had lain through her childhood. Sometimes they talked; sometimes Jane read aloud from her small red book of the Gospels; and sometimes she stood beside her bed looking down at the dress of soft black wool she would wear in the morning. Lovingly Mrs. Ellen had made it, edging the cuffs and collar with a ruff of white muslin.

Sleep came only very late and fitfully, and then Mrs. Ellen touched her shoulder. This was the day. Trembling seized Jane as she dressed, and she drew a blanket around her shoulders and gratefully swallowed the scalding milk Mrs. Ellen brought her. Then resolutely the tired girl closed her mind to all earthly things and concentrated on prayer.

At nine o'clock a messenger came from Guildford requesting a last meeting. But Jane, her calm re-established, declined to see him but sent an affectionate message reminding him that this was no parting since all eternity lay before them. Shortly afterwards the drums began to beat and the bells of all Hallows' and St. Peter-ad-Vincula to toll. Jane sank to the window seat. Guildford . . . the most innocent of them all, a boy whose only crime was having been Northumberland's son . . . Guildford, frightened, alone up there on Tower Hill. Her eyes filled and a tear dropped on the new black wool.

She wiped it quickly away and rose to leave the window when the rattle of a cart attracted her. She turned back out of idle curiosity, for something to do. A two-wheeled cart

passed beneath her window. In it, shrouded in a sheet, lay a crumpled figure. Sick and giddy, Jane shut her eyes. The drums and bells were silent. An execution had been finished.

She was still sitting quietly, beyond all feeling, when at last they came for her. "I am ready," she said to Sir Thomas Brydges, the kindly jailor, as he crossed the little room to her side. "Please take this. It is something I have found great comfort in these many years, God grant it comfort you, too, for your kindness to me." She put into his hands the little red volume she had carried so long, and the good man, his fingers trembling, his voice uncertain, took it from her. As he did, something fluttered from it and was lost on the dark carpet where it would be swept up with the dust of days. No one noticed the little dried leaf which on an afternoon years earlier, had dropped from a tree in the garden at Sudeley to settle beside a lonely child sitting on a stone bench. She had said she would keep it forever and had pressed it between the pages of her book. And today a pause between Now and Forever had come and the green leaf had become dust.

The drums began their rolling again and the bells their message. Walking beside her chaplain, followed by Mrs. Ellen and her ladies-in-waiting, Jane crossed the yard to the scaffold. Her head was covered by a small Tudor cap of black velvet and in the penetrating wind off the river her hair blew up around it in damp childish ringlets. Indeed, without her clogs she looked like a serious twelve-year-old, and a buzz of pity rose from the several hundreds of curious who had gathered. Ahead there was a short flight of steps and at its top a terrifying hooded figure clad in scarlet, the face masked.

Only Mrs. Ellen mounted the steps with Jane. It seemed the soft woolen gown must be removed after all, and the old woman's fingers shook as she unbuttoned it and drew it over the small proud head. Now for the required five minutes the prisoner must stand waiting for the traditional "pardon" which might (but never did) come at the last moment. The wind was bitterly cold whipping about the girl's bare shoulders and she bit her lips to keep them from trembling with the violent chill that shook her.

I must not be sick—I must not cry—if only my knees did not shake so. Bradgate, Sudeley, Hampton Court, little Lady Marjorie moving back into the dark after saying "We shall walk again together in the ways of peace," they all swam before her through the shadows that were shutting her in.

"Father—Father—Our Father—" she tried to make the words fall in correct sequence. Then with a noiseless, lithe step the scarlet figure was beside her and through the mask a muffled voice spoke not unkindly:

"Now, Your Grace."

Against a flash of steel those nearest heard a girlish voice cry:

"Father, into Thy hands . . . ."